TERRA BELLA

TERRA BELLA

A NOVEL

MONIQUE THÉORÊT

For Megan

*To cherish the remains of the Earth
and to foster its renewal is our
only legitimate hope of survival*
—Wendell Berry

Foreword

"This was not a time of accounting for our flawed nature, rather it was a time for lifting the veil that reveals our magnificence." These are Lilly Goodwyn's reflections, one of the central characters of *Terra Bella*. These words reflect the spirit in which this book was written.

Much has been written about the appalling state of the environment. It is not my intention to contend it is otherwise. I have been among the many who are deeply saddened, at times angered, by the unstoppable momentum that has led to the environmental crisis we are now facing. I have been among the many who have sought alternatives through lifestyle changes. And yet, within this genuinely concerned citizenry, for many of us our actions have been limited by a sense of powerlessness, our belief that the powers that be are much bigger than we are. Cynicism has found its way into our hearts and minds and has kept us paralyzed.

As I wrote *Terra Bella* during the time of the COVID-19 pandemic, I was motivated by these words: *If not now, when?*

These words resonate on both a personal and global level. My intention in writing this book is to offer potential solutions to a complex situation. I think of it as a teaching novel. A profound shift is needed if we hope to reverse the momentum toward self-annihilation. The ideas presented are by no means comprehensive. It is my hope that my readers will become curious about the ideas presented in my story; that intrigue will promote investigation and research and spark a desire to implement some of these methods; that they may spawn fresh ideas and new inventions in service to humanity and to regenerating life here on earth.

Old systems are disintegrating as they must. We stand at the cusp of a new era. It's an exciting time for humanity. It is a time for self-sovereignty, as I see it. The process can be frightening as we take back our power from many sources of authority; be it the advancement of our own genius, in the workplace, our healthcare choices, from the so-called experts across a multitude of disciplines and our personal relationships. It is often easier to follow than to lead. It's a time to go within and find our inner compass, our truth. It is also a time of honoring each other's truth, with an understanding that we each perceive reality from a different lens and unique perspective.

The book also presents an invitation to see ourselves beyond the limits of this three-dimensional reality. This honoring can only breed a rich diversity of potential solutions to the problems we are facing on a personal, spiritual and global level. It is time to move out of our comfort zone, to release our rigidity, a rigidity that is fueled by fear and replace it with a more fluid approach, in the process, recognizing everyone and everything's inherent worth. Unity is the evolutionary path we are called toward. To that end, I humbly offer *Terra Bella* as a one possibility among many. May it reawaken a sense of wonder for the lavish world which Providence generously offers as our wondrous yet temporary home.

Prayer of Gratitude

*W*e sit down to dinner and Catherine says, *Let's offer up our thanks for this beautiful meal.* She pauses and about to begin asks, *Would you like to offer up the blessing, Lilly?* This blessing has been offered at every meal at my grandmother's home since I can remember. The words come easily. *Thank you, Great Mystery, for all in creation who participated in bringing this meal to our table. Thank you for their time, their love, their service and their sacrifice so that we may be nourished and we in turn may be of service to others.* The blessing invoked, we turn our attention to savoring the meal before us.

Summer is in full swing so there's an abundance of just-picked vegetables and fruits; some from Catherine's gardens and others purchased at the local farmers market that she frequents every Saturday morning having mentally rehearsed what is available on any given week from March through December. She plans her meals on the season's current offerings: dandelions in the spring along with ramps and asparagus; lettuces and robust greens to purify the blood and awaken the body after winter's sedentary rhythms. But it is summer now and our feast is lavish: eggplant fantails, pesto pasta, heirloom tomatoes served with feta, Kalamata olives, fresh herbs, olive oil and a balsamic reduction. The grilled chicken breasts from our farm were marinated in olive oil, with lots of garlic, lemon slices and lemon juice. Berries are plentiful along with the super sweet melon that Catherine's neighbor raises. There are bowls of lemon curd, crème anglaise and whipped cream to compliment the fruit.

As I look out past the pergola where we are seated, there is plenty of evidence of Catherine's steadfast efforts; always the loving midwife assisting nature to bring forth her abundance. She studied and implemented Rudolf Steiner's methods over thirty years ago, his double-dug beds in evidence even now. She read Wendell Berry, later bolstered by Bill Mollison's permaculture and its departure from traditional agricultural practices. She's coaxed many winter crops by implementing Eliot Coleman's pioneering work with low tunnel houses and select crops that will withstand frigid temperatures. On her bookshelves, you'll still find copies of *The One Straw Revolution, Permaculture: A Designer's Manual, The Unsettling of America, What is Biodynamics?: A Way to Heal & Revitalize the Earth, The New Organic Grower.* These are shelved with Annie Dillard's *Pilgrim at Tinker Creek,* Thoreau and Emerson. This place is a tribute to her convictions; the importance of place, growth and renewal. Gratitude is woven into this tapestry. My grandmother is a mystic, a title she would not consider or openly claim. She has always approached life with reverence and a great sense of wonder, always on the lookout for revelation of what knowledge might yet be garnered from nature's unfolding mystery or apprehended in the unseen world.

The blueberries are plentiful now. There are varieties planted on the side facing the pasture that are native and more appealing to the birds. Just behind these on the side bordering the house and gardens, she planted varieties that appeal to the human palate. Ever the pragmatist, she sees this as an act of diplomacy and respect for all in creation who wish to enjoy them. Living in harmony, everyone and everything is nurtured and supported.

The brambles are the handy work of bird droppings and become habitat for mice and rabbits. The brambles create a natural fence along another border of the extensive gardens—nature's defense against early frost and wind. Unwanted scavengers who, having been plied with berries, are somewhat deterred before making their way to the Swiss chard, lettuce and leafy greens planted on the other side at the edge of the garden. Some sacrifices will be made; offerings of gratitude for all who contribute to making overabundance possible. The cycle of give and take is ever-present in Catherine's cultural practices.

This is the school room that I grew up in. The spiritual lessons were gleaned from the wilds: the birds, the four-leggeds, insects, wind, rain, sun, decay, death and renewal, excess and lack. I could not have been more richly educated and rewarded. In time, I would learn to appreciate this extravagance as my inheritance, Catherine often wordlessly supplying the wisdom. In that ubiquitous school room, a sense of wonder accompanied my playtime, my learning and eventually my work. As a child, I soon mastered the names of birds and their calls. I learned taxonomy as if by osmosis long before I could fully understand the meaning of the word, nature ever generous revealing its richness and secrets for the observant seeker.

And I would learn of nature's tempest, nature's torrent and nature's withholding and of her profuse extravagance. After nature's devastation, we witnessed nature's persistence and tenacity. Each season, its own spectacle offering up revelations, gems gathered along the path: hoarfrost, fog, ice storms, spring thaw, fireflies; the dismantling of milkweed pods in summer to reveal the mermaid inside; the song of the wood thrush, the mating dance of the woodcock, each informing of the splendor and the tragedy inherent in temporal and corporeal life. The lessons that would be thrust upon me as I stepped into adult life could not have been apprehended with curiosity, imparting their wisdom, had I been raised within the confines of a townhouse or the civility of town life.

As a girl, nowhere was nature's exuberance more apparent than in its flora. Learning the names of native plants and wildflowers eventually led to creating a unique calendar. Here, time is marked by the appearance and faithful return of native plants and wildflowers; their short-lived emanations adding to the wonder. This calendar departs from convention and begs tolerance for variance in the start and length of season from year-to-year. Where some might appear early one season, the previous season's insistence on remaining a week or so longer or passively moving on determines the emergence and fading of the next.

Should amnesia overtake me, I could name the season, regain my bearings by what my surroundings reveal: spring beauties, bloodroot, trillium, hepatica, trout lily, bluets, anemone, wild ginger, mayapple, blue cohosh, waterleaf, day lily, chicory, Queen Anne's lace, Joe-Pie-weed, ironweed and goldenrod, each in succession. The scent of the air lends confirmation; the cool earthiness of spring, the innocent, fragile growth that only spring can command with unwavering bravery on the heels of winter. In this often-short-lived season the miraculous occurs at such a rapid rate as to nearly become unremarkable; the fullness of summer punctuated by the rhythmic rasping of locusts at nightfall; the fecund sweetness of autumn, the vivid display of foliage in riotous colors as a final tribute before the fall, and winter's inertia soon to follow.

Winter offers its own magic; the frigid air deepening my awareness of my physical boundaries, a sharp demarcation of where I begin and where the environment envelops me. Bare trees and winter sunsets, the iteration of branches in ever-diminishing likeness reaching up toward the heavens perceived against the refracted light of the season; the earth tilted away, the oblique sunlight and atmosphere traveled produce winter's unique palette intensifying color often absent in this austere season.

Our guests have left and I sit here lost in pleasant memories; these were and are the architecture that informs and creates my perceptions, the blueprint that guides yet never insists. I was born an innocent, as we all are, then dwarfed and misguided by the conformity required by the world.

There are summer days when the light of the sun shines upon the grasses, the trees and fields with an intensity that lies beyond the ordinary. The hills and the marsh are charged with an energy that lies beyond the pale. My awareness is awakened; I am possessed by greater senses. I experience more acutely the colors, sounds and scents. In these moments, I am filled with immense gratitude; my heart swells and offers thanks to the Vast Benevolence that pierces and permeates this reality pouring its knowing into all things as if to say, *I am here! I am everywhere!* I can never predict these moments. This Intelligence knows no vanity and is unimposing by nature. It is up to me to pick up the trail, never knowing what gifts it may bestow or what deceits it will illuminate and then reduce to rubble. In this generous state, I regain a sense of who I truly am.

Just around the corner, I hear Catherine's voice; it's the retelling of a story often told, the unraveling of the prayer of gratitude. I pick up bits of the conversation; Julia, my daughter, is unknowingly being initiated. This rite of passage at the tender age of five is Catherine's expanding upon the prayer's meaning; the instruction, implications and responsibilities that lie within its invocation. As I listen, I remember when the lesson was first imparted to me, much in the same way Julia is now being instructed. Great Grandma, a modern-day griot, tells a tale infused with wisdom. It is a story of interconnectedness, of our place in an intricate tapestry, this web that inextricably binds the micro and the macro, abundance and scarcity, ebb and flow, contraction and expansion. These rhythms are never entertained in a dualistic framework, but as incremental movements toward and away from, cyclical in nature; rhythms long recognized by native cultures, a story embedded, rooted in their mythologies. Sadly, that rhythm has long been disrupted; marked by our departure, our slow and unconscious breach from our natural cycles, seeing ourselves as separate and above nature, reducing the aliveness of nature to commodities to be harnessed, subdued and modified for our benefit, missing the ramifications of these changes until reduced to obsolescence.

The young farming family just down the road. Catherine begins, *came from Honduras twelve years ago. They have worked since that time at creating a way to make a living that brings them joy and a way to support their family. They love gardening, raising chickens and goats. They work hard and their efforts are rewarded. They came from the outskirts of La Esperanza, a region where life is centered primarily on agriculture. The cool climate in this area makes it possible to raise strawberries, potatoes and apples, staples unique to that region. Here, they are gardeners and cheese makers. The goats were a new venture for them and with study and effort they have become skilled at creating what is called artisanal cheese.*

Now imagine, Julia, a day in the lives of the Solarzano family: up early during the growing season and working late into evening, Catherine continues. *They rely on the sun, the rain, the warmth and long days of the season to feed their chickens, their goats and their crops which in turn feed them and many of us. Without their dedication and labor, we would not be the beneficiaries of their loving efforts. Then, we must consider the soil itself, the tiny organisms and nutrients that make it possible for those strawberries, potatoes and other crops to grow and nourish us; and so, we thank all of them.* Catherine pauses now allowing Julia to take this in.

Soon the story will take a turn and Julia will be introduced to Rumi, the Sufi mystic and poet. For this occasion, Catherine will select his poem *Chickpea to Cook* chosen for the lesson it imparts about how we are all in service to one another. Later, Catherine will talk of the Farmers Market and the beautiful foods made available to us for our growth, so that as the prayer says *we too might be of service to others. And what is our unique contribution? How will we assist others?* Catherine will ask. *By doing what we love, Julia; doing what fills our hearts with purpose.* She will conclude for the night and pick up the thread at a later time, knowing the importance of repetition in keeping this knowledge present and alive.

Next time, the emphasis may fall on the goat droppings, chicken litter and worm castings and their contribution to creating a living medium and nourishment for seeds that grow into plants, herbs, trees and more seeds. She will explain pollination in terms Julia can appreciate and understand. The story will grow in complexity to match Julia's growing ability to take in more sophisticated concepts over time.

Roused from my reflections, I stand and make my way to Catherine's kitchen to clear dishes and put away the relished remains of our feast. As I approach the kitchen door, I hear soft laughter; Catherine and Julia's conversation has shifted to lighter matters.

Catherine's kitchen features a large work bench, its base salvaged from the dilapidated workshop on the farm. A two-inch maple butcher counter was created to cover its top. Repurposed and functional, it serves as both a preparation and eating area.

The kitchen and well-stocked pantry speak of my grandmother's love of cooking. When she undertook the restoration of our bicentennial farmhouse, she chose state-of-the-art appliances carefully selected and in keeping with the era and humble architectural style of our family home. Our family has spent many hours here preparing meals and preserving foods; it is a favorite gathering place. Many Sundays, like this one, are devoted to food preparation for our bi-monthly gatherings with neighbors and with old and new friends. Good food seems pivotal to these gatherings which pave the way to sharing life's happenings and discoveries and creating bonds of community. These are Catherine's most cherished times.

ℰᴂ

The ramifications of my education in Catherine's care as a child, created an insatiable curiosity that would lead me to explore the inner workings and splendor of this magnificent organic world, specifically, the tether joining the visible and the invisible. This inner longing would take me to Siberia, the Amazon River Basin and the Andes to study the medicine of the Shamanic tradition. My Western perspective would be challenged, my understanding broken open. A coherent vision would eventually emerge, a fusion of ancient knowledge, blending the sacred with modern day science. I would return to my Western origins with a fresh vision and with purpose. In the end, I would return to Catherine's farm with an agenda of my own, to build upon her empire, if only to add a brick or two to her well-established dream.

Now years later, I have people showing up for the opportunity to implement their ideas and innovations, not seeking or needing the accolades of degrees earned or acronyms to follow their names. They are motivated by invention, restorative solutions and service. They implement projects on a small scale, studied for their long-term impact and viability. Caution is informed by the disastrous results of the past so often driven by profitability, swift implementation and professed superior effects. They apply exacting scientific protocol, but before their projects begin to take shape, they already possess a vision and conviction that almost always proves out empirically. Intuition seems to inform their research before the process of proof begins.

There are times of frenetic activity when their projects are fueled by passion, the need to know if their hunches will play out, and the demands of the research. Preliminary results from their trials demand that adjustments be made, a new set of variables implemented based on small intuitive nudges the research subtly suggests; their need to know demands that they step into the unknown. When success is achieved, they celebrate wholeheartedly, offering support for each other's efforts and victories, all achievements equally acknowledged.

There are periods that follow where little activity is apparent. This seemingly passive period too is fertile; a gestation, a pause allowing for new inspiration to surface and take hold. Some take their leave, going off with backpacks and tents; some in groups, others alone. They leave for distant and remote places in pursuit of selfless endeavors; their destinations, where many live in poverty and remain dependent on international aid to feed themselves. They learn the language, become an integral part of village life, participate in ancient rituals. Their authenticity bridges the cultural gap. Once trust is established, work begins. They remediate habitat and implement soil-building methods, water harvesting and conservation. In time, perennial cropping and edible landscaping replaces what was once an arid and infertile landscape, adding beauty and providing much needed nourishment. Empowered and fed, the community is uplifted and inspired and moves from the cares of daily survival to entertaining further progress. A new vision for the future can now take root.

My own research is secondary now. My focus has shifted to mentoring and supporting this dynamic and inventive community. My task is to ask curious questions, fueling their imaginations. There is plenty of evidence to support that invention is sparked by a source beyond this tangible realm. And I am reminded of Catherine's legacy and the power of a simple prayer invoked at meal time and its capacity to awaken awareness and set change in motion in ways I could not have imagined or anticipated.

Meraki Project

*D*rew sat on the hillside with his back toward the wind. The sporadic gusts of wind informed him that the weather was changing, in all likelihood bringing rain. He would have to assemble the lean-to before long. At this altitude, preparations were a necessity for both him and the goats. There was an ideal spot halfway down the hill with shrubs and small trees that created shelter for the goats. And the wind, judging from the direction it was coming, would be marshalled and abated; the topography and air currents would keep the wind mostly above them. Drew was counting on the wind not shifting.

He sat gazing at the herd of three hundred cashmere goats, still feeling a rush of excitement and subtle disbelief that he had managed to bring all this about. The work was just beginning. He had yet to convince the villagers that the goats would transform their community from their long-standing economic struggles to a flourishing, vibrant village able to thrive; free to dream, to engage their energies beyond the necessities of survival.

Meraki was the name Drew had chosen for this endeavor; *meraki,* a Greek word meaning doing something with soul, creativity and love. It was an ambitious project which had taken two and a half years of preparation. Drew had spent a year in the Himalayas, in both Nepal and India; two arduous months with the Changpa, a nomadic tribe that inhabit the Changthang Plateau of Tibet, then on to Kashmir, to the major center of *pashmina* production, in the city of Srinagar.

The Cashmere goat produces a fine, downy winter undercoat which is highly valued and sought after in the fiber world. As the days shorten, the goat's undercoat grows; harvested as spring approaches, the *pashmina* as it is often called, is combed off the goats helping them stay cool in summer. Exploited for its commercial value, productive breeds were developed. Those suppliers, intent on maximizing production and profits, shear the goats so that the outer coat of coarse hair must then be removed. What qualifies as Cashmere must meet strict regulations with the fiber diameter never exceeding established standards. That approach did not meet Drew's criteria. In a closed loop system, everything worked synergistically and supported every part of the system. Shearing did not support the goats. Combs would fill the function of removing the fine hair without waste, both the goats and the villagers benefiting from this interaction.

Drew saw harvesting the fiber as a secondary benefit that the goats would provide. Yes, the fiber would be harvested, spun and woven, creating a valuable product that would benefit the villagers and provide additional income, but the Cashmere goats' primary role was to clear the land of noxious weeds on what had become non-arable land and assist in fertilizing the soil with their droppings. The Cashmere goat has an unusual predilection for consuming many tough native plants that do not appeal to other foragers.

The work ahead in preparation for another night in the rain and wind was of little concern to Drew, but the task of inciting the villagers to embrace this project had him nearly stymied; his concern noticeable in his dark blues eyes. The village shaman had welcomed him, having predicted his arrival. Paralyzed by a decade of poverty, inertia and entropy had set in. The exhaustive tasks of providing food, heat and shelter on a daily basis left little time and energy for contemplation and possibility. What was needed was a vision of a new future. Perhaps with the aid of the shaman and ceremony the villagers could be roused and mobilized.

Drew's heart constricted at the thought of the betrayal the villagers had suffered at the hands of the oil developers. The disillusionment that followed led to fear, destruction, mistrust and eventually paralysis; it shook the very foundation of their beliefs. Drew sat in meditation that first night camping with the goats and asked the question, can you suture a life back together after being decimated by repeated loss and disappointment? And the darkness responded with a resounding yes.

ↁ

The next morning, Drew and the dogs were on the move; it was time for the goats to forage and clear another portion of the pasture. Drew marveled at the triangular shape of the goat's head, its unique ability to strip the plants of their foliage leaving the stems intact. Were the stems cut, it would signal the plants to send up a new shoot, in essence strengthening them through adversity and becoming more tenacious; without leaves, no photosynthesis. The plants simply die, minimizing their ability to reproduce seeds that would have propagated when in bloom. In fact, whenever the goats were moved to a new location, the first thing they did was to snap off the flower heads. After just a few days of living with the goats, day and night in Tibet, Drew had noticed that the males, nannies and yearlings had their own preferences for plants as if each had developed a palate for specific plant species.

Looking at those triangulated shapes triggered a buried memory of his encounter with the *Mantis* during one of his Shamanic journeys. She appeared to him with her pointed face and wide set eyes, brilliant and dark. Her face was gentle, her headdress a rounded triangle of bright yellow veneer, the tip of which pointed toward her diminutive nose. The headdress was embellished with undulating lines curling on their ends; lines of blue and red studded with tiny sapphire and ruby crystals. Drew had no words to express the love emanating from her being. As she came closer, golden antennas appeared, their curled ends opening and reaching to connect with him. The first of these reached for his *Dan' Tien*, his lower abdomen, another attaching at the heart and the last at his third eye.

He felt a subtle and powerful energy pulsing through these thread-like connections, balancing and creating coherence between these centers.

Drew had no sense of how long this exchange lasted; he had entered a timeless dimension. Once she released him, he was bathed with an indescribable sense of peace and wellbeing, a state he had not experienced since his early childhood. For days after his journey, he experienced the world with fresh eyes, a new way of perceiving. For a time, the electromagnetic information coming in from the outer world was interfaced with an inner knowing, the information streaming in received from a neutral place, impartiality allowing him to operate from a higher state.

If Drew were to describe it now, he would attribute this experience to the shift that occurred moving forward. As the dreamlike state he had experienced subsided, his state of being remained harmonious, grounded and nurtured an expanding state of wholeness. It assisted him in tapping into other dimensions as lucid dreams became more commonplace for him. One foot in both worlds is what he had learned over time.

The dogs barking, bring Drew back to the present moment, his attention quickly shifting to the movement of the herd. He is suddenly reminded of the unique relationship of the dogs, goats and the goatherd, all the more important in his situation because of the lack of fencing. Yet the Changpa managed their herds without fencing. Theirs was a subtle communication that Drew had yet to master or fully understand.

❧

The villagers sat around a roaring fire in anticipation of the village Shaman's arrival. The new moon signals a time for planting seeds, albeit proverbial seeds this time of the year. The village men had gathered early preparing the fire and creating sacred space. The significance of this gathering was apparent to the village elders who had been in conversation with the Shaman since the last full moon gathering. The seeds to be planted were the seeds of the future.

The *Mapacho* ceremony that preceded the Shaman's appearance was coming to a close. Even the young children present sensed that the time had arrived to be silent, attuned to the proceedings about to unfold. As the Shaman entered everyone rose; he appeared clad in a ceremonial cloak and feathered headdress. Without pageantry, he approached the gathering and took his seat. He sat for some time in complete silence wordlessly signaling to all present to be very still, to shift their focus from their cares and their thoughts to their hearts, the place where all answers lie.

He began by sharing a vision of a decade ago when he first became aware of the difficult journey ahead for his village and its people. The siren song of progress had swayed some of them, and because of a long tradition of trust and cooperation, an agreement had been reached with the oil company. Through prayer and intention, the village had survived the complexities and disintegration that followed once the ways of the West had been introduced to village life. Much confusion had followed, some questioning the ways of the past, others vehemently rejecting the ways of the West. Division was inevitable. Dissolution had run its course and now the time had come to reflect and assess what had transpired and to decide on a course going forward.

Last time the village had gathered, the Shaman had told them of the man from the West who was coming to pave the way to a better life; a life that would require commitment, endurance and trust. The villagers, even the most devoted among them, had shifted in their seats, incredulous at the suggestion that a man from the West could possibly bring salvation, and be an instrument of meaningful change.

The Shaman began to weave wisdom into words. He spoke of transformation using age-old imagery that even the youngest among them could grasp. So, his tale began; he spoke of the birth of new ideas as a butterfly emerging into life. *The egg,* he said, *is the beginning of all things, is it not? What is yet to be born. It is where life originates. Faith, nurture and commitment become the fertile ground that allows the idea to take hold and develop; this is the larva stage. The cocoon stage means going within to develop this idea. Time must pass and allow for this process to unfold. All along the way, contained within the egg, the larva, the pupa, imagination fuels this transformation leading to the eventual appearance of the butterfly.* The Shaman paused, allowing for his words to take hold. *Emerging from the chrysalis,* he continued, *what was once a caterpillar now takes flight, a creature of the air delighting all with graceful flight and vivid colors. What was once a thought and imaginal is now a reality in the outer world. This is the process by which worlds are born; such is the power that lies within all of us. We are creators. Life never stands still; it is either evolving or decaying. So, it is with all of us, ever moving in never ending cycles of change. The question before us this evening is: Can we as a people discern where we stand? This is a very important question to ponder. Spirit has presented us with a worthy opportunity. How shall we proceed? Will we remain at a standstill paralyzed by the past, or will we dare to dream a new dream?"* The Shaman became silent, marking the end of his message.

The villagers sat bemused and uneasy. It was clear that oil exploration and illegal logging practices had been highly disruptive and destructive to the villages of this region. The villagers were unprepared for the devastation that took place once the Westerners arrived; they showed no reverence or connection to the land. Never once had they entered into ceremony asking permission of the trees, the streams and animals before tearing away at Gaia's flesh, creating wounds that would take generations to heal and perhaps for the spirit of the villagers to recover. Ancestral lands had been obliterated. The village Shaman was asking them to release the past, step into the future with the aid of a young Westerner. Could this blue-eyed, fair-skinned young man be trusted?

ༀ

The boys from the village appeared at the base of the hill just as Drew was finishing his breakfast. There were five of them carrying water, food supplies and sleeping gear. Where they were headed, Drew had no clue. At a distance, they appeared shy, quietly speaking among themselves apparently trying to reach a consensus. After a few moments, the tallest among them made his way up the hill. The boy made his way toward Drew's makeshift camp, occasionally glancing back at the other boys and then shyly making eye contact with Drew. On arriving, he greeted Drew in a strange dialect, a fusion of Quechua and Spanish. Drew picked up on the Spanish and was able over time to determine that the boys had been sent by the villagers to assist with the care of the goats. Drew interpreted this unexpected development as a sign that the village meeting with the Shaman had stirred the villagers to action. Drew knew it was best to proceed with caution, to be grateful and without expectation.

He signaled the remaining boys to join them. Once they placed their gear under the shade of the nearby trees they sat down, shy and silent. Drew passed dried fruit and jerky around the morning fire where they all sat. He brought out his drum and encouraged the boys to join in the singing of *Ikaros*. Drew could see the boys begin to relax and smile. Once a connection was established, Drew took the boys down the hill and introduced them to the goats; using Spanish and gestures, Drew established a dialogue.

In time, he would teach the boys about the importance of establishing communication with the herd and the dogs, albeit silent, yet essential. Five boys was a good start, Drew thought, but many more would be needed as fencing was not an option here. Containing the goats was the synchronized effort of goatherd, dogs and the goats, establishing a telepathic, silent agreement among them. For this to happen the goatherd had to become an integral part of the herd, establishing his place as the leader, the whisperer. Drew had experienced it among the Shangpa. This he knew to be the only possibility of maintaining a herd without reliance on fences. The boundaries were invisible and seamless. A great goatherd could set the boundaries and the goats knew, the dogs always obedient and eager to assist.

Drew went to sleep that night greatly encouraged by the day spent with the village boys and all he had managed to teach them despite the obstacles of communication. He hoped in time that he would find a way to convey that the goats have enzymes and bacteria that allow them to consume noxious weeds without ill effect, much like alchemy. Listening to the boys' native banter and soft laughter, he drifted off to sleep.

As Drew came to consciousness, he was surprised to discover the boys' disappearance. Perhaps yesterday had been intended as an opportunity to gather information to be shared with the village. How had they managed to pack up and leave without stirring him to wakefulness? Drew smiled in spite of his disappointment, remembering their curiosity and willingness to help with the tending of the herd.

It was a chilly morning, the sun coming up held the promise of a fine day. Drew dressed and threw a ball cap over his tangled blond curls, turning his attention to building a fire and preparing for the day ahead. As he finished his morning preparations, he heard voices behind him. Turning, he discovered the arrival of several new boys just as shy and tentative as yesterday's lot. Drew smiled welcoming them, inviting them to join him. So began a new day and the opportunity to establish a relationship with these village boys and through the boys, a relationship with the village and its inhabitants.

ℭ

Some months passed. Each day, the boys show up unfailingly. A group of twenty boys share the responsibility of tending the goats; five arrive each day. At first Drew was skeptical that they could manage the herd. After just a few weeks, it soon became evident that their Shamanic traditions play an important role in their skillful management, both telepathy and intuition woven in and directing their actions. One morning, the boys arrived with a cart. Drew looked on with curiosity, never questioning their actions as they unloaded rocks which they placed in the cardinal directions. Looking back, Drew could not recall an instance when stray goats had to be fetched once the rocks were in place. The boys were quick to learn. Drew recognized that he was being schooled in subtle ways and grateful for the opportunity; he could learn from them as much as they, from him.

The village girls began showing up in the Spring. Bois-
terous and unguarded, they were quick to make their wishes
known. They had come to harvest the prized Cashmere fiber.
Drew had had the foresight to bring back a quantity of tats,
the combs developed by the Changpa specially designed for
pashmina, the goat's fine undercoat. Drew demonstrated how
to use the comb even as his initial, awkward attempts met with
resistance from the goats. Drew looked on with wonder as the
girls took up the task with a quiet expertise that subdued the
goats and eased their task. Each carried a cotton sack strapped
across her shoulder and as the comb was filled, deftly removed
the fiber and stuffed it into the bag. They worked quickly,
their work punctuated by light conversation and laughter.

Once the fiber had been collected, the girls would return
to the village. The village women were already preparing
natural dyes, adjusting mordants to insure color-fast fiber
in an array of subtle and vibrant colors. There was much
animation and curiosity as they undertook this task for the
first time.

Drew noticed that festivities often accompanied collaborative efforts in the village. Many villagers had gathered early
that morning procuring wood and starting fires for the dye
pots. Some of the village women set about preparing food to
feed the gathering. As the women prepared, they took turns
singing, clearing old patterns and calling in healing from
the ancestors and unseen spirits to support their endeavor.
No project could possibly succeed without calling for their

assistance and guidance. Music and song were woven into every aspect of life, so in time Drew began to recognize them by name; *Intiq Churin,* Children of the Sun, was followed by *El Condor Pasa,* The Magic Bird Passes Overhead, and one of the older women followed with *Tarukaq Mosqoyning,* Dreams of a Deer. Many nights, Drew had lulled himself to sleep in the little hut that was now his home in the village chanting *Puka Pullera.*

The fiber would be washed and dyed, and once dry, combed. The Cashmere would then be ready for spinning and weaving. Within weeks, beautiful shawls, runners, blankets and wraps were woven and ready for the regional market in the adjoining province. Vivid colored skeins of handspun yarn were also piling up in baskets as the market season approached. The marketplace was a tourist destination where in years past the village women had taken their handwoven baskets, produce, seeds for exchange and hand-dyed and spun yarn. This would be the first year in nearly a decade that they would make the long journey and participate. The market had been shuttered nearly five years ago as the impact of logging and oil drilling had slowly eroded the surrounding villages' way of life; some were able to sustain some part of their livelihood, but each market season brought fewer numbers until it was no longer possible to attract buyers and visitors. The market reopening marked the beginning of a new era; this is the vision that the villagers held in their hearts.

಄

Over time, the men of the village had joined the boys and provided supervision and guidance, giving Drew the opportunity to work out a plan for the reclamation of the lands the goats were clearing. The forest margins had to be maintained, and carefully encouraging native shrubs and plants would assist in creating a vertical understory of foliage, pioneer plants and crops. The intention was to create beauty, reduce labor and assist in bringing plants, insects, and animals into balance; a dynamic system leaving nature to assume much of the work and maintenance and guaranteed to foster succession.

After studying areas that had not been affected by the loggers, Drew had a plan. Reforestation was also a monumental task, but already small nurseries were springing up in nearby villages, their efforts both necessary and voluntary. Saplings would be planted in the decaying trunks of harvested trees and *succession* would greatly assist their efforts.

By assisting this process, through mimicry and native plant selection collected from nearby undisturbed habitat, restoration could be accelerated. From there, nature would quickly step in, able to restore balance and a thriving ecosystem; the intention was to support increased biodiversity, create wildlife and plant habitat, enhance water quality and containment and soil fertility. The fields would be transformed by creating mounds, spirals and shapes with lobes that increase edges and make use of vertical space, creating stacking function, and reduce non-arable space with fewer walkways to access crops. Careful planning meant becoming intimately acquainted with the land: rainfall amounts, microclimates, drainage patterns, topography, slope, soil and weather patterns such as frequent frosts. Small scale agriculture would support the villagers and the surplus would provide a major source of income.

What had originally attracted Drew to this region was the rich heritage of the indigenous tribes rooted in agriculture. He had no doubt that their agricultural practices would still be in use had the mindless clearcutting and oil exploration been averted. What followed, massive loss of precious soil, extensive loss of habitat and flooding were natural consequences. Drew saw his efforts as a revival and a regenerative process not only for the land but for its people. He had embarked on this project to assist the efforts of the High Andes indigenous peoples to reclaim their agricultural and medicinal traditions. It was equally important that this revival occur within a historical context, bringing awareness and appreciation for their culture and traditions.

For generations they had held and transmitted ancestral knowledge about agriculture specific to their area and climate. Farming is a highly collective activity in this part of the Andes, enriched by the culture's age-old reverence of the land, Pacha Mama. She offers her living and breathing body and must be treated with dignity. Rituals had always preceded any endeavor; blessing the fields before planting, expressing gratitude for all that is and will be received, asking for guidance with right timing for planting and harvesting of the crops and medicinal herbs, and how much to take of the native vegetation so all relations are fed and honored.

The community persists because of its commitment to mutual help. A network of cooperation extends beyond the boundaries of their tribes and villages. They engage as they have for generations in seed sharing, labor delegation and the selling of surplus crops. They have created large seed fairs with both women and men involved in local and outside-community seed procurement. Their permaculture practices have persisted in spite of their temporary displacement during the *Green Revolution.* The small crop farmers had shown a healthy skepticism when the modern monocultural practices were first introduced. Many of them had adopted a wait and see attitude and continued with their traditional agricultural practices. Pure and simple, Drew had great admiration for these people and much to learn from them. What seemed most striking to him was the adaptation of these farmers to their environment.

Most impressive were the irrigation systems they had developed to deliver water to arid fields and to retain some of the warmth accumulated throughout the day. Irrigation canals were often angled around the mountains; these added a layer of protection to younger crops and tender roots. At these elevations, many environmental conditions had to be considered and mitigated from variable rainy seasons, soil conditions, pests and the necessity of diverse cropping.

Incan-designed terraces had been in use since pre-Columbian times; these terraces break up the cold air coming down from the mountains. The stones of the terraces also absorb heat during the day keeping the soil above frost temperatures. With the aid of intercropping, Drew knew that insect populations would be greatly reduced; he envisioned a synthesis of traditional and modern practices as the foundation of his revitalization efforts. He would experiment with low hoop houses as another method to forestall frost and look for plant species with proven vigor to extend the growing season.

∞

After nearly a year, Drew felt a part of the village community. He now observed a greater expression of joy, more laughter, and an ease among the villagers that had not been there when he first arrived. He felt deeply rewarded and eager to launch the next phase of the project.

Soon, Drew would be leaving, making his descent to the Amazon River Basin where he would seek out his dear friend, Paco, who until recently had been studying *terra petra*, mainly for its potential in sequestering CO_2. He was now working in the Peruvian rainforest with a non-profit organization from the US dedicated to reintroducing *terra petra* – a pit method of creating a highly stable carbon – to where it had originated in pre-Columbian times. Carbon is a fine-grained residue produced in the absence of oxygen by smoldering agricultural waste and excess trees created by covering the burning mass with soil. Paco had shared that adding *terra petra* to the soil creates a number of benefits; improving water quality and assisting in retaining water-soluble nutrients. It creates a habitat for beneficial soil microorganisms, increases soil fertility and plant health. Drew hoped to persuade Paco to join him in the village for a few months and teach the villagers this method.

Drew envisioned an exchange of labor and hands-on education which benefited both river and mountain communities. He saw river dwellers engaged in learning the benefits the goats offer in reclamation and land management and mountain dwellers learning the labor reducing benefits, water retention qualities, fertility and increased yields that *terra petra* adds to their farming practices. With increased soil moisture, their fields would require less irrigation and erosion caused by persistent winds would be slowed.

Since the discovery that *terra petra* was created by humans throughout the Amazon, hypotheses about the virgin nature of the rainforest have come into question. This soil differs considerably from the surrounding landscape supporting the idea that it was created by ancient Amazonian cultures. Building fertile soils allowed them to subsist in specific regions for extended periods of time. Scattered throughout the Amazon, this soil-building technique had been in use by groups of people for thousands of years. The previously scientifically-held views of the development of the rainforest were shifting since the discovery of this deep dark soil and its contents.

Paco's participation in the project was fueled by the realization that ancient Amazonians had lived for nearly 2,500 years in one of the most diverse and vulnerable ecosystems without ruining the environment. This ingenious soil improvement method meant they could grow a greater number of crops and added to the biodiversity of the ecosystem. Paco knew that finding ways to interact positively with the world around us was what was missing in modern day culture, be it agricultural, economical or sociological. He'd embarked on this project as an opportunity to give back what had been inadvertently taken from the indigenous people of this area. Could their efforts give back what had been lost during the Spanish conquest when their populations were decimated by the introduction of smallpox and measles?

By incorporating char from material they had burned into the soil, a habitat was created for fungi, bacteria and other soil organisms, improving soil quality and fertility in an area where temperatures, and humidity contributed to the accelerated depletion of available nutrients. Much of what these indigenous farmers had achieved had occurred through observation and a cooperative approach that was mutually beneficial -not the domination of nature that western civilization had employed for a few hundred years at an immeasurable cost. The ensuing degradation has brought us to the brink of annihilation. Extensive analysis reveals that wood and field waste burned into the soil, bone remains, pottery shards and animal manure are the ingredients that make up *terra petra*.

The ancient Amazonians over time had patiently created fertile soils and had found ways to live sustainably.

☙

The journey from the mountains to the lower elevations gave Drew some time for reflection. He looked forward to his time with Paco. They had met during a year-long *Shamanic* training in Mexico. The challenges of *Shamanic* initiation undertaken with this group had required rigorous self-reflection and had created a formidable community. The challenges had brought Paco and Drew together and a bond was established that went beyond friendship; over time they became brothers.

For a time, Drew had struggled with what he saw as social inadequacy, that his solitary nature was somewhat of a handicap that called for remediation. But as his attempts at becoming more sociable would reveal, his rich inner life and curiosity could not be traded for those happy gatherings among people on the fast track, steeped in a traditional lifestyle and prescribed outcomes. One evening of lively music, excessive drinking and awkward conversations about his career path and motivations left him particularly deflated. He came home and built a fire, knowing this to be a prescriptive to relieve his agitation, gazing at a star-studded, moonless sky.

In a more lucid state, surrounded by the occasional crackling sounds of the fire and the stirring of night life, he realized that he readily became animated, at times even passionately engaged, in the company of like-minded people. This insight brought him peace and his foolish attempts to fit in to a close.

Moving forward he understood that the people who were meant to be in his life would simply show up; he went to bed that night feeling relief. As was often the case, confirmation showed up quite unexpectedly a couple days later, while standing in line at the local coffee shop. The woman in front of him was reading as she waited. She held a bookmark in her hand with a quote by Aristotle, *"Whosoever is delighted by solitude is either a wild beast or a god."* Drew experienced a moment of euphoria and recognition on reading these words. Two months later, at twenty-two, Drew set out for Mexico, marking the beginning of his *Shamanic* path.

෴

Paco expected that Drew would arrive today; he was hoping he would arrive in time to witness the rituals and tribal ceremonies that precede the planting of crops. These ancient rituals call upon the interaction of humans, nonhumans and other entities to achieve continuity and regeneration. The forest spirit, Sachamama, is called upon as is Pacha Mama; gratitude is expressed for their blessings as is the water, fire and wind, each element calling forth fruitful crops. The villagers would offer Chichi, a fermented corn drink, and the vessels which hold the drink, broken and offered to the earth as the *terra petra* is spread into the fields. Researchers now suspected that this was the source of the pottery shards in *terra petra*. The rituals connected the farmers to the land, the earth revered as a living being and humans as one aspect of a living web.

Drew arrived later that afternoon long after the rituals, ceremonies and planting had taken place. There would be many more opportunities to participate as more fields were being readied for planting. As Drew approached the settlement, his eyes found Paco in the crowd of men. His small dark sturdy frame, jet black hair and lively banter brought back fond memories.

Paco and Drew stayed up late that first night reminiscing and sharing the details of their current projects. Paco was heading a funded program from the US aimed at developing Forest Garden techniques. With a generous grant, they were establishing a Permaculture Education Apprenticeship program in collaboration with a Peruvian non-profit group. The joint venture had acquired a parcel of degraded land and several students were living on the premises as the project was now getting under way.

Not only would they implement an agro-forestry program that students would help to design, they also aimed to preserve Shamanic traditions including medicinal plants and the techniques of *terra petra*. This program was collaborative in nature, designed to include the indigenous community. Their knowledge and ancestral practices would become the backbone of the methods employed and implemented. Once these systems were well-established, they would create multi-layered sources of income for the local community. At that point, the organization would step away and turn it over to the local inhabitants. They could continue to provide the apprenticeship program to regional and students from abroad as a vital permaculture model while adding another source of income.

Drew and Paco exchanged a great deal of information and had reached collaborative agreements. Drew felt more enthused and determined than ever to implement the next stage of his vision on his return trip to the mountains. Twelve years had gone by since his time at Catherine's Farm. He found himself drifting back to those days and the events that had led him to his decision to drop out of university and turn his attention and energies to this tiny program implemented by Lilly Goodwyn on her grandmother's farm in the Midwest.

He'd set out for university in the West at eighteen filled with optimism. He saw both the town where he was headed and the university he would be attending as models of innovation. It was not long before he began to understand the limitations of philosophy and academic pursuits not grounded in hands-on applications. Drew felt that lecture halls and information were incomplete. Without application, one could not deepen one's knowledge or marry the intangible to the tangible; in his mind knowledge would always remain a precursor to experience.

As for the town, it proved to be equally disappointing; in spite of what initially attracted people here —the rugged mountains and abundant sun— the town's architecture was

cold and sterile. Every available bit of space was eyed specu-
latively for further commerce and megalith homes aimed at
creating a false sense of worth and status. Enterprises were
created to indulge all appetites for fine things as an end in
themselves, which seemed to Drew expensive indulgences and
distractions that encouraged an outwardly-focused sense of
worth. At the end of his first academic year, he left. He had
read an article in a self-published permaculture publication
that had featured Catherine Goodwyn's Farm earlier that
spring. This had led to first-hand inquiries and in-depth
conversations with the program director and his eventual
decision to join the innovative hands-on program as soon as
the semester was over.

෴

He arrived in late spring and was greeted by Lilly and her
then thirteen-year-old daughter, Julia. It was late afternoon
and at a short distance, Drew saw that dinner preparations
were underway in a substantial outdoor pavilion equipped
with a wood-burning oven & grill, refrigeration and water. A
playful group of young men and women were busily attending
to preparations. A sense of ease and comfort permeated the
atmosphere. Beyond the food preparation area, he noticed
round wooden tables arranged in a semi-circle near a stone
fireplace, the chimney insulated and extending beyond the
vaulted ceiling vented well above the roof. The tables were
decked with seasonal wildflowers in canning jars and large

hurricane candle holders with beeswax pillars. This is where the group retired after dinner preparations and a long day's work to feast and recreate. Dinner inevitably shifted to easy and animated conversation about the day's challenges, discoveries and victories. Music and levity often followed.

Drew was introduced to the group and offered to join in the preparations. He was given the task of preparing a salad; there were spinach, pea shoots, tatsoi and roquette washed and ready. With a spiral cutter, he created ribbons of daikon radish and just-harvested multi-colored carrots which he added to the salad. He was handed a small round of bleu cheese wrapped in cheesecloth, produced here on the farm to add to the salad. He had begun by rubbing the wooden salad bowl with a clove of garlic; his last addition was the toasted and salted pumpkin seeds, no doubt a product of last fall's harvest. The nutty, rich and pungent flavors called for a mustard vinaigrette which he would add just before serving.

As he lay in bed later that evening, recalling the dinner and conversations informing him of the extent of the research that was happening on this two hundred-fifty acres farm, he felt a surge of excitement. He'd been skeptical that the program would live up to its espoused mission, but as he sifted through the evening's events unable to sleep, he felt optimistic that his ideas would not be immediately dismissed; he sensed he would be encouraged to implement them on a small scale and later evaluated for their merit and practical application. Drew would later learn that this process would be supported with valuable suggestions to boost results and overcome challenges.

At the heart of it, the program rested on one foundational premise. Catherine, the program's founder, had always encouraged participants to turn to nature for answers: *Become very still and observe; here you will find the solution to whatever challenge you are facing,* she frequently stated. *Life requires all of us to acquiesce to a participatory relationship with all of Creation, intuiting our role in the web of life; the Sacred must inform our thoughts and hearts and precede any action.* She referred to the process as 'listening to the language, the voice of nature.' Once Drew asked her pointedly just how she accessed this information. She replied, *you engage in what I call a Morse Code with the Universe; Tap! Tap! Are You there? And then patiently listen.* She went on to say that the answers did not necessarily appear immediately, but her antenna was up, in receiver mode, and then returning her attention to whatever was at hand, an insight would inevitably surface under the unlikeliest of circumstances, perhaps that day or some days from now or during the night. *At times, all that is needed is the ability to surrender,* she'd concluded.

At first look, her demure figure obscured the sharp intellect and wisdom that became evident whenever she spoke. She spoke with economy, a function of the wisdom garnered over the course of ninety years, no doubt supported by the knowledge accessed and gained from previous lifetimes. Drew always loved her unannounced appearances in the outdoor labs or during an evening gathering. In her presence, one's senses were heightened. One felt that she might almost disappear in her moments of silence, fading in and out; here, but not here.

One night Drew unexpectedly happened upon Catherine walking her beloved dog, Sky. He fell into step with her as they walked the trail leading to the edge of the sugarbush. At ease in each other's company, they walked mostly in silence appreciating the changing colors of the sky, the day shape-shifting into night. As they neared Catherine's home, she invited him in for tea. Drew was surprised at the ease with which they slipped into conversation, seated on Catherine's front porch that evening. She sat on the wicker chaise, her wispy grey curls stirring in the soft evening breeze, delighted by his company and now eager for conversation.

Drew spoke of his early childhood experiences, that his curious nature had been nurtured and encouraged by his parents. He shared the details of one of his earliest experiments. He'd been convinced that stone walls facing north could be utilized to provide a natural means of cooling a room in summer. His father had shown a great appreciation for Drew's innovations and offered to help him to build a rudimentary structure that incorporated the natural stone face. They had framed three sides, created a roof and soon were busy with siding; they'd included salvaged windows on all three sides. The next phase of the project was redirecting runoff to the rock wall from a nearby stream, the water being gravity fed to the wall. The challenge here would be to control water flow, a factor determined by rainfall; locks and dikes to divert overflow had to be considered. Too much water and evaporation could not be controlled.

On the roof of the small cabin, Drew and his father had installed a south-facing solar panel. On a structural beam spanning the width of the cabin, Drew had mounted a series of small solar-powered fans, the heads pivoted toward the engineered waterfall, the presence of air adding to the evaporative cooling effect. The fans could either oscillate or the fan's air flow reversed so that the cooling effect produced by evaporation could be directed into the room. He'd also insisted on mounting lights that were directed toward the rock wall having a free and reliable source of energy in place. This decision was purely aesthetic in nature.

To complete the project, they would dig a shallow trough, line it with spouting that would act as catchment for excess water flow at the base of the stone wall. Drew had seen the possibility of in-home application of his system by mounting stone slabs onto the wall and eliminating the need for a water source by adding a trough at the base; the addition of a small pump circulating the water, created a feedback loop. This system would require a water filtration system or the use of distilled water to eliminate mineral build-up that could clog the system. His ruminations brought a smile to Catherine's face; she appreciated his inventive nature.

છ૭

As Drew neared the village, he was filled with anticipation, eager for what felt like a homecoming and to learn what had transpired during the six weeks he'd been away. The children greeted him with smiles and happy shouts as soon as they spotted him. Drew's heart swelled remembering the hesitation and fear that he'd immediately sensed, their unguarded reluctance to welcome him on his arrival more than a year ago. Embracing their spontaneity and warm welcome, Drew expressed his appreciation by breaking into a dance that the children joined in as they made their way to the village plaza.

The next morning, Drew was up early, eager to assess what had transpired during his absence, anticipating the inevitable changes brought on by this expansive season and the villagers' work and participation. But the villagers had other plans for Drew that day. It would become a day-long event, a celebration of his return. Several boys were at his door, waiting for him as he stepped out, a delegation with a mission to escort him to the plaza.

Cooking fires had been started and the noon meal was already under way. Familiar aromas were wafting and co-mingling in the air evoking memories of past celebrations, the scents intensifying as the group neared the central pavilion. The men greeted him with warmth and respect displaying genuine affection. The women were more reserved but equally welcoming. The morning's activities were punctuated with laughter and playfulness.

As the tables were laden with the midday feast, Drew noticed that many dishes indigenous to the Andes were represented. There were many sauces, *Aji* scented with garlic and onions, *Salsa de Chochos, Peanut Sauce, Cheese Sauce, Ensalada de Berros,* wilted watercress salad, *Relleno de Flor Nabo,* field mustard blossom stuffing, *Sopa de Olluco Con Papas,* Olluco Potato Soup. *Olluco* also known as earth gems are only surpassed by the ubiquitous potato in Andean cuisine, both rich in protein, amino acids and minerals. There were bowls of *Quinoa Leaf Puree, Tangy Quinoa, Chupe Verde, Papa de Rellena Con Cuy,* Potatoes Stuffed with Cuy; *Lupin Bean Casserole with Chicken, Oca Chicken Stir-Fry, Hulled Barley Tortillas* seasoned with cilantro, onion, garlic and carrot and *Field Mustard Tortillas;* there were amaranth and corn pancakes, *Tortilla de Maiz Y Amaranto* along with *Potato Tamales* and *Quinoa Banana Cakes. Quesillo,* a fresh style cheese, was introduced to the Peruvian Andes by the Spanish conquerors and was generally an addition to traditional dishes often found in sauces and stews for flavor and texture.

For dessert, there was *Rallado de Arracacha,* a sweet paste made from *arracacha* cooked in cane syrup, dessert crepes made from amaranth and quinoa served with *Mazzamora de Ayrampa – ayrampa,* the deep red berries harvested from a thorny bush often turned into jam; *Mazzamora de Flor de Nabo,* field mustard pudding alongside the much-loved *Chuno* pudding also known as *Lupin Delight* or *Mazzamora de Chuno.* Lupin and quinoa flour were often turned into gnocchi or sweets. Today they were offered as *Galletas de Quinua,* quinoa cookies and *Potato Kisses.*

Eating, playing, singing and dancing made up the day's activities, the villagers naturally giving themselves over to this joyous occasion. After the meal, the village center came to life with K'antu, the ancient style of music and circle dance native to the Peruvian Highlands. Young and old partook in playing *Siku,* the panpipe, *Quechua qina,* the traditional flute of the Andes, guitar and lute. The youth were partial to *Nueva Cancion* and were given an opportunity to give interpretation to old songs and introduce new pieces. Drew was reminded of a Rumi poem as he listened to the music: *Don't worry about saving these songs. And if one of our instruments breaks, it doesn't matter. We have fallen into the place where everything is music.*

The festivities lasted well into the night, and as night approached, activities shifted and unwound to fireside story-telling and quiet reflection, families eventually taking their leave and retiring to their homes. That night, Drew easily drifted off to sleep in a state of contentment and with a sense of wholeness. Free of the enticement to ruminate, having been fully immersed in his moment-to-moment experience the day had unfolded, he felt deeply satisfied.

∞

The previous day's festivities had given Drew occasion to walk on the village paths that led to village homes and gardens. A mix of adobe and stone houses lined terraced streets and were traditionally roofed with thatch from Ichu grass, creating dry and warm homes. Some two-story structures sported tin roofs. Many homes had adopted perennial cropping and edible landscaping. Bright, sunny yards were festooned with the bright purple blooms of lupins, the underground bean later harvested for consumption. Medicinal and culinary herbs were growing by kitchen doors. On the side of many houses mashua could be seen climbing on trellises; a member of the nasturtium family whose orange flowers not only added beauty but also provided tubers and edible leaves and blooms. Inter-planted with beans, potatoes and corn in sunny backyard gardens, the mashua offers protection from nematodes, fungal diseases and some harmful insects. Birds were frequent visitors as were flying insects and bees each contributing and receiving from these living landscapes. In tree-shaded corners, he occasionally spotted brightly-colored hammocks. Everywhere he looked, he saw function and beauty, a fusion that supported the villagers both physically and spiritually.

Julia

*J*ulia grew up on Catherine's farm. From the time Julia arrived in this world she and Catherine were inseparable; true Spirit Sisters. As an infant, Julia became animated and lit up in Catherine's presence. They had a sacred agreement, to love each other unconditionally. They had their own special communication; one or the other could launch into conversation mid-thought and the other understood with no need to fill in the blanks.

Julia was initially home schooled and could not remember when schooling had officially started. As a two-year old she was learning about birds, flowers, the seasons and the stars. She spent hours in her grandmother's library perusing books and frequently coaxing Catherine away from her desk and farm accounts with an alluring title and a glance. For a time, she loved an illustrated children's version of the Greek myths. Among her favorites was the tale of Atalanta, the beautiful goddess who could run faster than any man and the story of Arachne, the skilled spinner who because she was boastful was turned into a spider. They spent several months reading *The Arabian Nights*. Catherine's version had beautiful full-page illustrations by Maxfield Parrish. Julia never tired of looking at these magical renderings. *King Beetle-Tamer* was a bedside favorite as was *The Seven-Year-Old Wonder Book*.

Later, as she began to direct her own education, she turned her attention to the writings of Henry David Thoreau and other American Renaissance writers; Emerson, Whitman, Harriet Beecher Stowe. There was a large collection of art books; the Impressionists, Klimt, Picasso, Steiglitz, O'Keeffe, Ansel Adams, John Sexton, Wolf Kahn. Her favorite among all of them was the illustrated works of Andy Goldsworthy. Julia loved his short-lived installations fashioned from rocks, ice, leaf litter and lichen; each borrowed from nature and inevitably subjected to impermanence.

There were books on feathers and bird guides for locations across the globe. She found books on rare animal breeds, alternative farming methods, quantum physics, and ancient civilizations. There was a section devoted to language; volumes exploring the advent of the written word beginning around 500 BC and its impact on the separation that was inadvertently created between subject and object. Catherine appreciated the written word as a great advancement for civilization, a means of preserving wisdom and transmitting knowledge, the access and freedom it generated and the empowerment it provided to all classes. But sadly, the age of literacy had initiated a breach between mankind and the rest of creation. A shift had occurred that inexorably delivered us to our current day view hellbent on and blindly immersed in separation.

For Julia, the library was a treasure trove. One day, she found a section she'd never taken notice of before; the lower left side of the bookcase that spanned the entire wall floor to ceiling, somewhat concealed by the reading chair set by the window. This area was entirely devoted to mystical writings. She found seminal works by authors unknown to her at the time; titles authored by Joseph Chilton Pearce, Robert Woolf, John Muir and Jean Liedloff. One stood out because of its mysterious title, *The Coming of Wizards*. Shelved among them were numerous translations of the Sufi mystics, Rumi, Hafiz and Kabir.

❧

When Catherine had first returned and assumed responsibility for the running of the farm, her efforts had been focused on the land and its revitalization, providing a living for her and the people who made this a reality. Once systems were in place, she turned her attention to the care of her family's Midwestern farmhouse. Her ancestry was catalogued in the many rambling additions that had occurred over time.

Catherine's aesthetic led to changes that create a more cohesive look. She designed an addition with a natural patina that belied its age, by carefully selecting untreated and antique materials and letting nature assist. This was her beloved library.

As for the house's exterior, much of the clapboard was replaced and an extended porch gave the more recent additions more pleasing proportions, as though planned from the beginning. A new roof tied everything together. Catherine spent a small fortune on new windows. At her insistence, the multi-paned windows, wooden sash and mullions were reconstructed to maintain the character and feel of the house. The exterior was painted a sagebrush green; she selected a butter cream tone for the windows and pilaster style casings. The 200-year-old antique heart pine floors throughout the house attest to the multiple generations who called this place their home. Catherine went to great lengths to bring them back to life. She hired a crew to finish them first with tung oil and then treated with carnauba wax to preserve their surface patina.

Inside, she maintained many of the wooden plank partition walls. The edges were interlocked in a tongue & groove joint and in places the decorative running bead remained. Catherine assumed artistic license and widened doorways where she could, adding French doors to bring abundant light into the house. The rooms were painted in a complimentary palette of spring green, robin's egg blue, sand and cream while natural wood surfaces added warmth and a sense of well-being to the house.

The library had special meaning for Catherine; this addition was her most cherished project. This was her place for contemplation, in her library she rested and found respite from the cares of the world. Over time, Julia would spend countless hours there, in Catherine's company.

She searched and found wide heart pine boards for the library floor. Her great indulgence was an oversized many-paned window reaching from floor to ceiling. She placed her vintage writing desk and chair by the window where she could enjoy the view and the shade of the nearly three-hundred year-old oak. The massive oak served as a constant reminder of the old-growth grove she visited frequently. The remaining walls were lined with floor-to-ceiling bookshelves, the shelves made of one and half inch thick alder designed to hold a substantial collection of books. She decided on a vaulted ceiling, to give the small room a spacious feel while adding rough-sawn barn timbers to give the room more substance.

Her great extravagance while updating the house was rebuilding and widening the fireplace in the living room. For this project, she bought a lot of used bricks and an antique mantelpiece which were in keeping with the period of the home at a local auction.

༄

As a young girl, Julia could often be found sitting outside absorbed by the colored plates of a favorite bird field guide. Julia loved birds as much as her grandmother did. For hours she listened to recordings of bird calls, already familiar with numerous species. She loved the anticipation she felt as she heard the bird prior to seeing it. On one occasion, Lilly spotted her in the shade of the wisteria that climbs the pergola situated near the east entrance to the house.

They easily fell into conversation about Catherine's travels to Belize, Costa Rica, Peru, and Australia in pursuit of some elusive species and to add to her bird list. Already at ten years of age, Julia yearned for such an adventure. Catherine had taken her to Point Pelee for the warbler migration two years ago. She had marveled at Catherine's ability to hear the bird and then tell Julia to train her binoculars at two o'clock where she might spot a blackburnian warbler, black and white with flaming orange on its throat and crown. She remembers now the feeling she experienced at first sighting it. With Catherine's help, she had learned to hear the *teetsa teetsa teetsa teetsa zizizizi* of the blackburnian and the *weeta weeta wetsee, weeta weeta with-chew* of the magnolia warbler. From that moment on, hearing a bird created a surge of joyful anticipation.

She smiled recalling her adventures with Catherine who could suddenly show up at the house asking if she was interested in chasing down the Sandhill cranes her birding friends had spotted in a nearby marsh. Nearby sometimes meant a fifty-mile trek in inclement weather. Once there, it was not unusual to wait patiently in the cold or rain for hours donning gumboots, a parka, and gloves along with a thermos of tea for warmth; hopeful the birds could be spotted, crouching among reeds, being very still with binoculars scanning the water and the sky waiting for their appearance. These conditions never deterred Catherine or Julia. On the return trip there would be lively conversation about their sightings while they ate hearty sandwiches and hot soup from thermoses.

From early spring, there were days designated to searching for and identifying wildflowers, her mother's passion. This way of learning was invaluable. She would immerse herself in locating and identifying the native flora with Lilly's guidance. Both would marvel and be uplifted by the exquisite beauty and intelligence, the vibrancy evident in a myriad of forms, shapes, colors and fragrances; profusion and adaptation in the name of preservation.

These forays in nature were often followed by journaling and drawing; identifying the reproductive system, noting the presence or absence of tendrils, exploring the function of the parts; the types of leaves, the flower parts and their arrangement. This led to drawing and explorations with pastels and water-colors. From a single activity others spawned, adding layers of information in a way that was visceral, educational and creative. At the deepest level, the lesson imparted was a reverence for nature. From there one easily slipped into a mystical awareness where mutuality and reciprocity could be experienced. Nature offers her own language, a language of revelation.

Julia had a great love for feathers and rocks; She began collecting them as a young child. Each held a fascination for her and her curiosity for them never diminished. She was captivated by the intricate designs of feathers. Could mutation really be responsible for such divine creation? Could a lizard scale through natural selection have generated a thing of such exquisite beauty and intelligence? Or had a leap occurred, winged creatures taking to the skies, spontaneously appearing, an imaginal birthing into form from the Great Beyond born of a burning desire?

From a young age, she began to collect feathers that she found on her walks in the woods, on the streets, at the edge of a pond or lake. Her room alone could not contain them all and they found their way into vases, display boxes mounted on walls, onto every surface that Lilly would allow given the extent of her collection. Julia studied them with a magnifying glass to take in their intricate details and coloration; the flame color of the Baltimore Oriole and the iridescent shimmer of peacock feathers captivated her; the iterating patterns of multi-layered feathers designed to adorn or camouflage. She marveled at the bird's inherent capacity to finesse a landing, true masters of maneuverability.

Then there were rocks. They could be found anywhere; at the ocean, in the mountains, when turning soil. The mica that shimmered, the nugget of garnet trapped in granite, her endless passion for quartz. At first her search did not extend beyond what could be found. And then she discovered gemstones.

☙

Julia spent countless hours playing with the Solarzano children. They went fishing, collected pine cones and rocks. Julia recalled one summer day they had collected prickly burdock blooms and fashioned them into tiny furniture and animal shapes. They rode on bike trails through pristine countryside stopping to look at trees, wildflowers, streams, listening to and locating birds. They challenged themselves to races and cartwheels and ever-expanding physical challenges.

Julia would sometimes join them in their daily chores; milking the goats, feeding the chickens and weeding the garden. They picked strawberries, raspberries, blueberries, peaches and apples throughout the growing season and often manned the farmstand that serviced both the Solarzano's and Catherine's Farm. They'd created a joint venture that was mutually beneficial, increasing the diversity of products they could offer and the advantages of shared labor and lowered costs with a shared facility.

Rosa, the eldest daughter, had introduced Julia to spinning using a drop spindle. Catherine's herd provided the wool. Julia was shown how to use hand carders, combing and aligning the fibers and creating *rolags* for spinning. They would clean the locks, removing the weeds and seeds and load them onto the carders. With the carders they combed and aligned the fibers, creating light airy rolls ready to be spun. They preferred to spin *in the grease;* they both loved the benefit of the lanolin which softened and nourished their skin. Julia associated the warm, soothing feeling she experienced while spinning with the scent of the wool and lanolin. They had studied plant-based dyes and began experimenting, eventually creating skeins of yarn that they sold at the market stand.

☙

One day, Julia arrived home and announced that she wanted to go to school; her friends did, so why not her? Lilly was not surprised by Julia's request. She knew that inevitably the question would come up and was worth exploring. That evening, Lilly sat with Julia and put forth a plan. They would contact the local school and request a tour; Julia would attend for a few days and then decide if this was the right place for her to continue her education. They would also visit the local Waldorf school and Julia would explore that as another possibility. Lilly made the arrangements starting with the public school the following week.

Lilly could sense by the end of their visit to the public school that Julia already had her doubts about being confined to a seat most of the time, the inability to take a break when needed or stay with a subject until she was satiated. School seemed very rigid to Julia, but she was not dissuaded. She would attend school as agreed and move through the disciplines and the set schedule and see how it went. Two days were all Julia needed to determine that the school's restrictions were too confining; she felt like a caged bird.

Several days went by, Julia basking in her freedom and newly-found appreciation for her circumstances and her self-directed education. Monday arrived and the scheduled visit to the Waldorf school. That morning, Lilly sensed Julia's reticence as the time approached for their scheduled meeting. Julia's sense of honor would not let her back down and so off they went as planned.

The initial meeting aroused Julia's curiosity as they discussed a self-paced approach. She was encouraged by the relaxed atmosphere she witnessed as she circulated several classrooms. The children in attendance seemed happy, relaxed and enthusiastic. The school provided both knowledge and experience, a garden, a kitchen, spinning wheels and looms, a huge art room. Julia noticed that lessons in chemistry were woven into a baking class. Math, fractions, ratios and physics were explored while measuring ingredients for pastry, as were the effects of convection heat and humidity.

Lilly sensed Julia's excitement on the drive home; still, Julia remained silent and non-committal. She showed up for breakfast the next morning dressed and ready to go. No words were offered, but her excitement was palpable. This day would mark the beginning of Julia's Waldorf education.

❧

At thirteen, she became greatly interested in sustainable systems, a natural outgrowth of her home environment. Biodynamics was taught at the Waldorf school and a recent class project and subsequent research led her to the discovery of Rudolf Steiner's *Domes* and Mike Reynolds' *Earthships*. These discoveries ignited her passion for whole systems solutions, her relentless pursuit of sacred geometry and Vedic architecture. These disciplines would later become her means of expressing her gifts.

That summer she attended the *Biotecture* program offered in Taos, New Mexico. She had convinced both her mother and grandmother that this was a worthy pursuit and they had encouraged her to apply when her interest persisted. She worked through the obstacles that her age presented; she had written a letter to the founder.

Her letter included many technical merits which showed her keen understanding of ecology. She made no attempt to subdue her idealism; she expressed her confidence that *Biotecture* would make a great contribution to alternative and sustainable architecture going forward. She spoke of her family's school and the many ways it contributed to her education. She'd included a photo of herself in an effort to remain transparent about her age. Her long blond hair, strong jaw and bright blue eyes conveyed her joy for life. A week later, she received a reply; Mr. Reynolds had personally invited her to join the summer session.

Julia settled into her summer living quarters in Northern New Mexico's High Desert, Lilly flew home the next morning. Julia spent the next ten weeks learning about the design and construction of passive solar homes. This approach was a radical departure from conventional architecture. Homes were constructed using natural and upcycled materials including earth-packed tires. They featured self-contained sewage treatment and water recycling, water harvesting and long-term storage, the use of south-facing glazed walls and in-home organic food production. The energy sources for home use included thermal and solar heating and cooling, electricity generated by sun and wind.

Over time, through experimentation and trial and error, *Biotecture* would create homes with no power lines, no gas lines, no sewage lines coming out, no outside source of energy and seventy-degree year-round indoor temperatures. At times, glass bottles were incorporated into the outer wall construction providing diffused natural lighting to the home's entryway. The bottles created a mosaic effect that was pleasing to the eye especially when multi-colored bottled and imaginative patterns were put to use. Large planters were strategically placed near the kitchen and bathroom sinks for use of waste water.

Julia felt she had entered a magical land, homes for fairies. She had, hadn't she? After all, the founder had written a book titled *A Coming of Wizards.* She went to bed every night happy and exhausted. Her education that summer extended beyond sustainable design and construction as she found herself in the company of a multi-generational and multi-cultural group of enthusiasts and free-thinkers.

The project she had volunteered for the following year included a fireplace; the owners choosing it more for its charm and ambiance than as a necessity. No additional heat was needed in this design. Adobe-like walls were formed around earth-rammed mortared tires creating thermal mass that regulated indoor temperature while skylights provided additional light and captured and released heat as needed. Julia was partial to multi-tiered round structures with gently sloping or domed roofs. She found them pleasing to the eye especially when colored bottles were an integral part of the design with thoughtful repeating patterns and deliberate placement, lending these structures a Persian look.

After three years of volunteering for *Earthship* projects she'd become very knowledgeable and grew to appreciate the systems at a new level of understanding. Julia had devoted many hours during the past year to studying water conservation. Her focus this time was on the water catchment aspect of the *Earthship* design, what Mr. Reynolds referred to as '*Water from the Sky.*' With the world already experiencing water shortages and an ever-growing world population, Julia knew that water conservation was imperative. This system offered a solution even here in the desert. Water was collected and used wisely; downcycling water for plants and treatment applications that created a living filter system referred to as *botanical cells.* These plant cells utilize the *grey* water for growth, then flow to other plant cells. Whatever remains is captured and routed to the toilet before exiting to a sewage system.

Once this project was completed, she would be off to Oregon to begin her post-secondary education. She was about to begin a three-year immersion in *Vedic Architecture,* an ancient and sacred building method that dates back to ancient India. Vaastu, as it is known in India, is steeped in sacred geometry, astrology, exacting measurements, the four directions and the elements. In this tradition, homes are designed to support its inhabitants emotionally, financially and spiritually.

Lilly

illy was thinking about the word *impressions* and how our thoughts, experiences and emotions create them. The higher the emotional amplification, the greater the impression. She knew that thoughts precede feelings and their intensity and frequency create neural pathways that become part of our patterning and define how we apprehend the world. She was convinced that they were also physically embossed, producing an unseen relief map with depressions and elevations, old wounds hidden until brushed up against. She found herself thinking *'I am a window'* as a reminder to allow her moment-to-moment experience flow through her, neither grasping nor resisting, being a witness with her heart open. It had not always been so.

When she was nine, Lilly came to live with Catherine. Her father, Fynn, had died tragically in a car accident when Lilly was five. Her mother, Olivia, was paralyzed by her grief. The sudden loss of her father and Olivia's inability to offer support left Lilly unmoored as if she had lost both of her parents. Family members had stepped in offering support knowing that with time their loss would be contained and life would resume a new rhythm. After two years, it became apparent that Olivia did not have the resilience to move forward. Catherine had stepped in and offered to have Lilly spend her summers at the farm.

Lilly arrived timid and withdrawn. Catherine took her everywhere she went. They collected the eggs from the hen house, fed and groomed the horses, worked the farm stand and cooked together. That first summer, Lilly slept with Catherine. Lilly never found words to express her gratitude for this generous gesture; next to Catherine she fell asleep feeling safe and cared for.

As summer came to a close and the time grew near for Lilly to return to her home in the Berkshires, Catherine saw Lilly's despondence grow each day. Although it was heart-wrenching to witness her granddaughter's growing agitation and reluctance to go home, Catherine felt the necessity for Olivia and Lilly to mend their shared wound. After another year, it became apparent that Olivia was unable to shake off the emotional paralysis that had seized her soul with the loss of her husband.

The following summer, Lilly came to live with Catherine; what was still considered a temporary arrangement soon became permanent. Quite unexpectedly, Olivia met a man that summer and within weeks she had come to the decision to join him at his home in Australia. There had been no discussion of Lilly joining her; Lilly felt both relief and sorrow when her mother told her of her plans during an unannounced visit in late summer.

Because of the great distance, visits were few over the years. Lilly experienced bouts of abandonment, betrayal and anger over the years, but with Catherine's assistance she learned forgiveness and self-compassion, the balm she needed to release herself from her past. Catherine was so full of life, it would have required a giant effort to remain downtrodden; and in time, Lilly lost her self-imposed introversion and began to bloom. Nature, innovative farming methods, the exciting learning environment Catherine created, and school dominated her life the next few years. She grew up confident and relaxed.

❧

Every morning, Lilly awakens just prior to sunrise; she steps outside and offers prayers of gratitude to Ra, the sun, and Gaia for yet another day of life. She expresses her gratitude to the sun and the earth for she knows that without them and their selfless generosity, life would not be possible. Deep within, she knows she is a dazzling embodiment of frequencies: light, geometry and sound coalesced into form.

She stands filled with wonder and awe. She is an expression of Infinite Intelligence, an intelligence she cannot claim as her own, rather moving through her even in her least conscious moments. She knows she can access ever-greater degrees of this Intelligence the more she stays aware, by being conscious of when she slips into states of frustration, the emotions triggered by disappointments and the stories she's created in her mind. She's made a great deal of progress in this respect and finds that she can now catch herself slipping into these states and can make a conscious choice to disengage.

After her extensive studies and travels Lilly had been drawn back to the farm. The farm then grew to include an onsite permaculture program with applications in a broad range of projects for a diverse population. In the last decade, she joined third-world non-profit organizations and collaborated on reestablishing age-old farming methods that had been abandoned in more recent times in remote regions of the world. The intention behind these projects was to encourage and assist in reviving the rich heritage and the agricultural practices of indigenous cultures abroad; these programs were designed to reconnect them to their age-old traditions and provide them with a source of income and much needed nutrition. She continued to travel to third-world countries and assisted in launching a number of women's cooperatives allowing women to utilize their skills, thus creating a global textile marketplace. She was an advisory board member for an organization that promoted ecotourism. More recently, she had been involved in fundraising to assist her former student, Drew, launch the *Meraki Project.* In September, she would travel to Peru to meet up with Drew and Julia who would be visiting Machu Picchu on the last leg of Julia's fifteen-month journey as she completed her research on sacred sites.

There was yet a deeper motivation behind Lilly's humanitarian efforts. It was a recognition that indigenous cultures had maintained a relationship with the earth that was participatory and inclusive. She was convinced that the loss of their way of life and their wisdom traditions should be understood as the extinction of a species. To Lilly this represented the loss of a golden thread that would not be easily retrieved, leaving us with guesswork at some later date, reliant on the conjectures of an archeological record.

A deep-seated intelligence might forever disappear, severing yet another tie, a life line that was so vitally needed now more than ever. She was willing to go to great lengths to revive and maintain this way of life; they were the wisdom keepers and she saw them as our teachers. From her perspective, we needed to become a multi-lingual species, learning the wordless language of trees, of water, of the land; learning to harmonize with all things. Learning to pause, to listen, to humble ourselves and ask for assistance from the life forms that have been here far longer than we have; allowing this billion-year-old process to inform us and guide us in creating systems that are regenerative, inclusive and mutually beneficial.

Lilly recalled the summer she met Langston. She was attending a post-graduate summer intensive in the Pacific Northwest. The two-week long program focused on the relationship between science and government policy. There were several presenters each day across a multitude of disciplines. Langston was a guest speaker, a researcher in the field of Restoration Ecology.

Langston was a dynamic and engaging speaker; he was also a realist. He spoke at length of the intersection between science and policy, particularly policy makers. What was needed was the skillful art of massaging them with facts that left little room for debate, he suggested. His style of communication was both direct and persuasive. As his lecture continued Lilly watched his tall lanky frame move with ease from his power point presentation to his audience. His movements were agile and fluid. She would later learn that he was an Aikido practitioner of many years.

His sense of humor made it possible to entertain his findings without losing heart. His research showed that promising methods for restoration were constantly emerging, but that policy makers still mostly gave lip service to implementing restorative alternatives to water processing, sewage treatment or capturing run-off. He explained that by implementing water catchment, downcycling waste water coupled with an engineered network that directed and diverted the *grey* water to parks and commons and then connected to sprinkler systems another tier of use could be implemented, eliminating the use and expense of treated water, a one-use option. Instead, it was routed to treatment plants or released to streams without mediation, introducing toxins, salinity and inorganic substances that impacted the biota and balance of these ecosystems. He outlined a multi-tiered system to eliminate water shortages by catching, storing, using, reusing and treating water creating an inventive system that fundamentally mimics nature. He was an innovative and elegant thinker. He had the ability to distill complex information in clear and concise language, shedding light on elaborate processes.

After the lecture, she was drawn to a group of people deep in conversation, elaborating on Langston Roarke's inspiring talk. The lecture had stimulated a lively discussion. Without turning around, she suddenly sensed that he was standing behind her; she turned. He stood there, his smile warm and playful, relaxed and inviting. A flood of emotions rushed up as she said hello.

At the end of the day, as the lecture hall was emptying, he'd made his way to where she was sitting and asked if she would like to join him for dinner. She accepted. Dinner paved the way to lively conversation, exchanging of information and a plan to meet up again soon. The frequency of their conversations and time spent together grew quickly in spite of the physical distance separating them, he on the West Coast, she at the convergence of the Midwest and the East.

From the time Catherine met Langston she sensed the inevitability of Lilly and Langston coming together, long before they would entertain the idea. Both seemed oblivious to the joy and excitement they felt in each other's company. Catherine guessed they both needed time to trust this feeling could live beyond the glow of novelty, the prism of initial attraction.

Langston's visits to the farm became more frequent and lasted longer. At last, they were ready to cross the bridge both had known for some time was inevitable. The breadth of the work at the farm and Lilly's responsibilities left only one option open to them; Langston would move to the farm. He traveled for his speaking engagements and his consultation work he could manage remotely from any location. He also traveled for several weeks a year when large projects required him to be on site. This new arrangement meant both could remain engaged doing the work they felt passionate about and now share a day-to-day rhythm neither had anticipated would bring them so much joy.

Life with Langston was an adventure; they sailed, traveled to pristine and little-known places, they rode horses, explored caves, climbed mountains; they read Aurobindo together. He was driven by a sense of curiosity just as she always had. He invited her into realms of thought that she'd never entertained before with *what if* questions. Once, he introduced an idea that blew her perceptions into another orbit. She understood that in the quantum realm we are both receivers and transmitters. Up until now, she had entertained quantum entanglement in terracentric terms. Langston now introduced the idea that our responses to our experience reach into the depths of the cosmos and create a feedback loop, that Source not only provided information but adapted, shifted, based on the information that was transmitted back. Before this moment, she had failed to comprehend that every thought, emotion and action affected the whole of the Universe. This new understanding begged the question, what do we wish to communicate?

For weeks she became preoccupied with this idea. Not only are we speaking, but the universe is listening, she thought. We are in fact co-creators *in-forming* the cosmos; this perpetual process fueling further expansion. What if by raising her frequency she could access even more *in-formation* from the Cosmos, she thought. And furthermore, what did she wish to communicate with the All? What if she or anyone for that matter, could activate a Divine Pattern held in waiting, much like the pattern of a plant held in a seed; a tiny seed filled with potential, eager to come forth under proper conditions. Surely, a similar pattern existed within us. What was needed to activate this pattern and reach fulfillment? What if this unconscious striving, this unnameable yearning, became a conscious striving toward this fulfillment? What if we realized that this Pattern was emergent in all things? Would this new awareness provoke a newly discovered reverence for all of life? Would this revelation awaken a sense of awe for all creation? She now entertained individuation as a facet of a hologram, the hologram of the Grand Cosmos, a particle that forms the waves and the wave itself, the waves of this Great Cosmic Dance.

☙

Julia was conceived a couple years later and came into this world just weeks after Lilly & Langston had celebrated their wedding with an intimate gathering of family and friends. The guests arrived several days before the ceremony. There was an ease to the preparations and each day brought its own form of celebration; festive outdoor meals prepared by friends and family; fireside chats deep into the night; wine, music and dance, quiet hours of reading and deep relaxation. After several days of ease and merry making, it seemed that the purpose of celebrating Lilly and Langston's wedding had already been fulfilled and yet the wedding day was one that would live in everyone's memory for some time.

The wedding was a day-long celebration; the festivities began early in the morning. For the occasion, four venues had been created at various locations on the farm, each with its unique atmosphere and purpose. The large open-air round-house that usually held straw and hay had been cleared of its contents. The wedding ceremony would take place here. The open sides were draped with gauzy-white fabric that floated in the breeze. There was an array of colorful woven rugs covering the worn wooden floor. The students and interns at the farm had gathered grape vines and turned them into loosely-woven balls of varying sizes. They'd inserted tiny white lights into these and hung them from the rafters in groupings of three. The larger ones were positioned by the posts along with potted trees and plants. A half-moon platform had been created for the ceremony, the floor covered with natural fiber rugs and sheep skins. An altar sat toward the back and the wall behind had been created with yards of apricot-colored raw silk fabric. Chandeliers were alight with periwinkle blue and tangerine-colored candles and vases were filled with wildflowers from the farm and the Solarzano flower gardens. Chairs for the guests had been set out in semi-circles, alternate rows staggered so that each guest had a view of the altar creating an inviting atmosphere.

Guests arrived and were seated and soon entertained by a group of dancers on the stage. The dance marked the beginning of the ceremony. The dancers were accompanied by live music: Andean pipes, hand pan, drums and Native American flute. As the dance ended and the performers left the stage, Catherine stepped up and read a Rumi poem in honor of the bride and groom who stood at the entrance to the wedding venue. As Catherine stepped off the stage, Lilly and Langston slowly made their way down the central aisle.

Lilly wore a simple white linen dress and a beautifully embroidered full-length shift. She carried a simple bouquet of brightly colored wildflowers. Langston wore casual linen pants and a Neru-style silk shirt. They graciously took the time to acknowledge their guests as they casually made their way toward the altar.

The nuptial ceremony followed and was performed by a dear friend of Lilly's, Enrique, a Huichol Shaman she had studied with for years. The ceremony began with a tobacco offering; the vows they exchanged were heartfelt and reflected their mutual respect and the integrity they brought to their relationship. The ceremony marking the joining of Lilly and Langston's lives concluded with the exchange of rings and a ceremonial dance by the bride and groom.

The guests had been asked not to bring gifts but rather to offer their blessings with a prayer, a reading or a small performance. After these presentations, Lilly and Langston presented gifts to each of their guests to express their gratitude for their presence on this momentous occasion and the gift of their friendship. As the ceremony concluded, guests were invited to make their way back to the pergola adjoining Catherine's home for brunch and libations.

The meal had been planned as an earth-to-table feast, nearly all ingredients used in preparing the meal raised and harvested at the farm. There were fruit and herbal infusions in beautiful colors in tall ice tea glasses, bowls of fresh fruit, frittatas, pan-fried multi-colored potatoes, fresh greens and arugula, savory mushroom tarts, fresh breads baked in the farm's brick oven, mujadara with crispy onions, pear and squash soup, sweet potato and ginger soup, plum tarts, grilled polenta cake with fresh cherry sauce and lemon coconut cake.

The meal was enjoyed at a leisurely pace with much intimate conversation and reminiscing. From there the guests were directed to a distant location on the farm to a grove of oaks where everyone could relax in the shade and share time together. Horse-drawn wagons were available for the trek, while some guests elected to walk, taking in the beauty of the farm.

There were chairs, blankets and free-standing hammocks in the grove and bottled drinks had been set in a nearby spring. Guests arrived taking in the majesty of the three-hundred-year-old oaks and the welcoming coolness of the shade. The mood turned serene and conversations were subdued; some dozed or napped, this segment of the day giving everyone the opportunity to assimilate the late morning feast.

As mid-afternoon approached, the guests were invited to make their way to the next venue. The wagons would escort them to the two-story historic barn situated at the northwest entrance to the farm. They arrived to the sounds of a band tuning up. The floor of the old barn had been cleared, long lines of couples were formed and a caller began to show the guests the steps to the first dance. The caller explained that *Contradance* originated in the colonies and became a fusion of English, French, Irish and German country dances. Each dance had a figure that allowed couples to dance up and down the set, the repetition of the figure giving dancers a chance to master the steps as they progressed down the hall, sitting out briefly as they reached the end of the set and then dancing their way back up. The music was lively, the band consisting of a hammered dulcimer, fiddle, guitar and piano player. Some were eager to learn while others hung back watching. Once the first dance was over, everyone was eager to find a partner and join in. After several lively sets, the caller asked for a waltz, giving everyone the opportunity to catch their breath.

After two hours of dancing and music, the wedding guests, bride and groom made their way back to the pergola for the evening meal. Glasses of wine and champagne were passed around and toasts were offered to Lilly and Langston, their life together and the imminent arrival of Julia in the not-too-distant future.

A dinner of grilled meats, fish and vegetables made up the evening meal. In spite of its simplicity, the meal featured numerous international flavors. For dessert, the gathering enjoyed homemade ice cream, sorbets infused with fruit, teas and herbs and shortbread cookies with rosewater glaze embellished with rose petal confetti.

At dusk everyone headed for the pond. Solar lights marked the shoreline providing ample light as the sun dropped behind the horizon. Guests paired up and boarded the canoes; everyone paddling to the center of the pond and forming a circle. Each boat held tiny wooden canoe replicas that held a votive candle. At the appointed time, the candles were lit and the little boats released to float on the water. The tiny boats bobbed on the nearly still pond, the candlelight reflected on the water. The darkening sky was lit with stars whose reflections could also be seen on the water's softly undulating surface. Shimmering gold and white lights stretched like ribbons across the water.

Each canoe also held a tiny pail filled with wildflower confetti, these were cast aloft toward the couple, the multi-colored petals landing like jewels on the water. An invocation soon followed; Enrique, the Shaman, called on the Cosmos to confer Its blessings upon the beloved couple's union. Everyone's gaze turned to the heavens; the wedding had been timed around the Perseid meteor shower. And now the skies provided the magic and the fireworks, the clear skies adding to the auspiciousness of the occasion. Everyone became very still and a sense of awe and gratitude seemed to permeate the atmosphere. After a time, a sense of completeness fell over the gathering and the boats slowly headed back to the shore. Back on the shore, Lilly and Langston thanked their guests for a memorable week of celebration and prepared to leave for the secluded cabin where they would spend their wedding night.

❧

The weeks following the wedding were dedicated to preparations for Julia's birth. The birth of their daughter had a profound effect on Langston and Lilly. The birth itself and the days that followed Julia's arrival were a time when they experienced a deepened sense of the sacredness of life. They looked to her to quicken their understanding, to plumb the depths of creation as she, so newly arrived, was still connected to the realm beyond. They learned from her how to enter into stillness and remain there for prolonged periods, losing their sense of time. Her curiosity as she apprehended the world was a renewal for both of them of the magic infused in what at times had become mundane and ordinary. Julia's presence brought to life a new awareness lighting up parts of their being, their moment-to-moment experience that had been dulled. What had lacked luster now appeared luminescent. Julia became the sun upon which their days rose and set. The months that followed were a time of unimagined discovery for both Lilly and Langston.

The morning of the birth, Lilly woke at dawn with early labor contractions. As she sat up, she felt the warm wash of amniotic fluid flowing in a pool around her. She gently woke Langston to share the news. Within the hour Catherine and the midwife had been called. The last-minute necessities were gathered and Lilly, Langston and Catherine leisurely made their way to the yurt where the birth would take place.

They had planned for a water birth and had transformed this space usually devoted to solitude and meditation to a birthing room. They had stacked wood just outside the entrance to the yurt in the event the early fall weather called for heat. They had rented a birthing pool that was positioned at the center of the yurt under the domed skylight. Towels, blankets and other necessities had been put in place in the intervening weeks as preparations had begun. The space itself was serene and welcoming; plants, soft fabrics and sparse furnishings creating a contemplative and natural environment.

Langston helped Julia get comfortably situated, relaxing on the upholstered chaise near the window before attending to filling the birthing pool. Towels were placed in easy reach of the pool and a carafe of water and glasses were placed on a small table nearby. Catherine filled the diffuser with water and pine essential oil for its strengthening capacity. Candles were lit. Langston and Catherine made their way over to Lilly; all joined hands and they offered a prayer for a smooth and auspicious birth and the welcoming of Julia into their lives. Lilly wanted to walk, so they set out on the path along the edge of the woods, Langston and Catherine at her side. They paused during contractions giving Lilly support as she focused her breath and allowed gravity to facilitate her labor.

On their return, Natalie, their midwife, greeted them. She'd arrived while they were out walking and was attending to further preparations for the delivery. Langston helped Lilly undress and enter the pool. The warmth of the water immediately helped Lilly to relax. The atmosphere was serene and happy. The delivery moved more quickly once Lilly entered the pool, contractions coming more quickly. Langston had showered and entered the pool when the delivery seemed imminent. As Lilly pushed Julia out of the birth canal, Langston gently brought their beautiful daughter to the surface, supporting her as she floated, taking in her first breaths. Julia floated on the surface of the water until the umbilical cord stopped pulsing. Natalie then attended to the cord and placed Julia in Lilly's arms; silence fell over the room and a sense of awe permeated the place.

From the moment that Julia had exited her womb, Lilly had stepped into a state of being that she could not have anticipated. Whatever effort the birth had required had immediately lifted and was replaced by buoyant joy. Julia was placed in her arms. The room became imbued with light; the light seemed to be emitting from within her, from her daughter and wherever her gaze fell. Everything became love. Lilly remained in this state for hours long after Catherine left and Langston stretched out on the bed next to her had fallen into sleep. In spite of the long hours of labor, the desire for sleep evaded her. She basked in euphoria, her heart wide open.

Months of adjustments and contentment followed. Julia accompanied Lilly and Langston wherever they went unless she was in the care of her beloved great-grandmother. Catherine and Julia were twin flames; one could feel the bond, the soul agreement that existed between them. A rhythm soon set in that was mutually supportive and rewarding. It wasn't without its bumps in the road, but solutions were found to accommodate everyone's needs.

The following summer, Langston set off for his sailing retreat without Lilly this time. She stayed behind with Julia; June was a busy month on the farm. This would give Langston an opportunity for solitude, a reprieve from responsibilities, time for introspection and replenishment. He returned tanned, relaxed and eager to be home, reunited with his family. The year that followed had a fluid rhythm as Julia grew into a toddler, Lilly and Langston sharing parenting to accommodate their work responsibilities. Catherine seemed more youthful after Julia's arrival; the two spent many hours together exploring the farm, in Catherine's library and gardens. In June, Langston left for his yearly oceanic retreat.

Langston's disappearance was a shock. Lilly remembered the Coast Guard's arrival which was disconcerting, but never had she expected to hear that his sailboat had been found with no one on board. There was no evidence of foul play. The weather conditions had been ideal during his time near

Martha's Vineyard which added to the mystery of his disappearance. In the end, they surmised that in some haphazard way he had slipped, hit his head before falling into the sea. For Lilly, life became surreal as though the earth had slipped from its axis. It was as though her feet failed to purchase the ground beneath her feet. There was a dizzying quality to every waking moment.

Langston had come to her in a dream the night before the Coast Guard had come. He was playful and filled with contentment as he approached her. He'd cupped her face in his hands, tenderly gazing into her eyes, telling her all was well. She'd awakened so content, feeling whole, expecting him to be there next to her. She lay awake for a while looking forward to his return in a few days' time.

Langston's time on the boat was a yearly pilgrimage, a sacred time to be honored, a time to replenish and reflect. For him the *Mirabella* and the ocean were a conduit, a portal for this process. The moment he stepped onto the boat his energy shifted. From that moment forward he operated on *Indian Time*; no clock, no devices, no contact. He ate when hunger informed him, he slept when his energy waned and the day felt complete; he awoke and rose as he naturally came to consciousness.

This had been the way since he'd been a boy and had joined his grandfather, Garrett, on these ocean retreats. Sailing, fishing, quietude; the panoramic view encouraging a more expansive state allowing for a sense of stillness and immensity to replace focused attention and the minutia of day-to-day responsibilities.

Lilly was determined that Langston's death would not be her undoing. For Julia's sake, she would not allow herself to withdraw from life and atrophy, unable to move on as her mother had. She had learned much from Catherine; she'd lost her only son, Fynn, as suddenly as Lilly had lost Langston. Catherine had made room for her grief, never crowding it out. Relief came for Catherine in remembering what a gift life is, that loss and its crushing pain were the other side of the immense love she had experienced as a mother and later the great friendship that unfolded between them. The loss was not to be questioned or resisted; she chose instead to indulge in gratitude for the gift she'd received, however long it had lasted. His departure had quite unexpectedly brought Lilly into her life.

Lilly awoke each morning determined to leave this prison of grief and rise in spite of the weight of inertia that pressed her downward, gravity exerting a greater force than she'd ever been aware of. Could she befriend grief as her grandmother once had? She would navigate this unforeseen season of her life with as much grace as she could garner on any given day. The presence of her beautiful daughter, Julia, like a winged Pegasus drew her to the surface; the purity of her unchecked joy and animation moved Lilly toward the light and the undeniable motion and rhythms of the living.

World Trek

Julia boarded the plane in Zurich, her last stop before journeying to Machu Picchu. Her visit to the Goetheanum felt bittersweet, bringing back memories of her days at the Waldorf school and her introduction to sacred space. The last fifteen months had been a world trek from Mongolia to Stonehenge, the pyramids of Egypt and Konya to visit the tomb of Rumi. She'd spent time with Hopi elders in the Southwestern US and revisited Serpent's Mound in honor of Catherine, her great-grandmother. She now recalled traveling to Adams County for the summer solstice. On that day, Catherine had explained, the sun aligned with the ball in the mouth of the serpent, as though the serpent was about to swallow the sun, symbolic of the marriage of earth and sky, the union of heaven and earth. Now she was headed for Lima and on to Machu Picchu where she would meet up with Lilly and Drew. She couldn't think of a better way to conclude her research on sacred sites while in the company of her mother and someone whom she considered a dear friend. She would be returning to the farm after their ten-day visit to Machu Picchu and traveling up into the Andes to the site of *Meraki Project*.

As Julia drifted in and out of sleep on the first leg of her international flight, she found herself reflecting on her vision. She intended to create a village. It would be an assimilation of the knowledge and wisdom she had acquired through intensive study and spiritual immersion. The next few months would be devoted to putting her vision down on paper. She would outline her intentions and the principles of a regenerative community. She would draft the steps needed, to bring it to reality. She would need the assistance of a number of knowledgeable people across many disciplines. She wanted to introduce a new economy based on gifting and exchange with a bank that traded community services.

Her architectural vision was a fusion of Vedic architecture and Earthship construction. Homes, offices, places of business would be designed to support the occupants physically, emotionally and spiritually. Structures infused with sacred geometry: cardinal directions, water flow and room function to support inspiration, abundance and a thriving community. Those who have more would give more, understanding that success is a privilege and a responsibility. The principles of potlatch would be part of the Community Articles. The community would be multi-generational drawing from a diversity of experience and knowledge. Schools would be hands-on, the expertise provided by the community members, giving them an opportunity to share their gifts and financially supporting them through their contribution. In-depth programs would be offered across the arts, astronomy, quantum physics, small scale permaculture, cooking, languages, textile production, house design and construction to begin with. The village would become a model and in time the expertise they would gain through the process of creation, of trial and error could be taught to others seeking to create community based on similar principles.

As she came to consciousness once again, she recalled her most memorable Shamanic journey. She remembered drifting away, finding herself underground and slowly rising above the surface of the soil, reaching toward the light. She instantly knew herself as the soul of a tree. She felt her roots reach down into the earth where a symbiotic exchange was taking place between her roots and the rich microbial life surrounding her, a mycelium network, in this moist and nurturing environment. She was compelled to reach upward and downward in equal measures, her roots anchoring her and moving her toward further expansion, while her limbs and leaves reached for the light and swayed in the breeze. Both environments were equally nourishing and inviting.

The life below ground fascinated her and aroused her curiosity. She was aware of being a part of a teeming community, a rich communication system connected her to neighboring trees, roots entwined. Communication and support flowed continually along this communal root system. The surrounding forest to which she belonged operated as a whole; all for one and one for all. She felt this soothing energy flowing toward her and simultaneously away from her, the two, inseparable. She understood that no barrier could ever interrupt this flow. She was equally connected to the trees at the edge of the forest as she was to those in her proximity.

The feeling of belonging was beyond anything she had ever experienced as a human; nor could she fully express it into words. It was as if having traveled many lifetimes in search of home and at last arriving, resting in the experience of unspeakable love, unspeakable peace, unspeakable sustenance. The experience never left her and created an unquenchable yearning to recreate it within the human experience. As days passed, her mind drifting back to her journey, she recalled having read a scientific paper on the relationship between galactic cosmic radiation and tree rings. She also remembered that in the Druidic Tradition, Celts revered trees, the Druidic alphabet represented by species of trees. She remembered reading about tree aerosols and forest bathing research. The research demonstrated that time spent near to trees increased immune system regulators, decreased stress levels which in turn reduced adrenaline and cortisol levels. Tree compounds released into the air were loaded with antibiotics, anti-inflammatories, antiseptics and antivirals. Living close to trees had shown that it could increase life span. Her journey had created a deepened sense of reverence for trees. She saw them as a gift.

The night before leaving Mongolia where she had immersed herself in the Shamanic practices of the Tungus, Gaia had come to her in a dream. She appeared as the goddess

Flora dressed in greenery of fantastical colors and shapes, gilded in sunlight, her solar plexus reflecting the crystalline nature of her central core. Water flowed from her hands and her slightest movement stirred the air around her. Birds gathered near her and then took flight. Trees, branches and leaves made up her hair. The sun and moon and starlit skies flashed in and out as though day and night occurred outside of time. The stillness was palpable.

Gaia was speaking to her, telling her that the Intelligence that sustained the forest, the awareness and connection she'd experienced during her journey was possible for humans. Julia was being asked to pave the way forward. The experience had been profound and seemed always to be just below her conscious awareness, beckoning her as she moved through her days. The dream was a vivid reminder.

In the days that followed, Julia grappled with the mandate cast upon her; a task at once noble and yet unspeakable and ephemeral. At times, she felt overwhelmed by the responsibility placed before her. Could we expand and create a field beyond our physical senses that allowed for communication beyond words and experienced as a wordless and visceral knowing; an intuitive and telepathic realm where comprehension bypassed intellectual interpretation, an untapped and unapprehended intelligence that had always been there just outside our reach? Until now? Could the imaginary walls that had been erected by the surface mind dissolve? Could she be ferried to that land at will, by desire alone?

In her finer moments, when doubt dissipated, she suspected that previous civilizations had functioned in this state, living in harmony for the benefit of the whole. If so, that information was available in the Field, the dark fertile Void, and could be accessed if her desire to do so was great enough, if she focused her intention and her heartfelt emotions fueled her desire to know. At other times, she wondered, had we arrived on this planet with those abilities? Had we arrived more attuned to our *Light Bodies,* unsequestered or anchored to our physical form and so more readily able to maintain our connection with Divine Order and Universal Law? Did they act both as a transmitter and a receiver? If so, when had we lost these abilities? Had we in times past been able to effortlessly tap into Universal Mind, All That Is, to support our journey and live from a place of knowing? When had intuition been silenced, dismissed as a trusted source of information? Her query kept her up at night. Had the onset of the *Kali Yuga* heralded a time of vibratory dissonance, a slowing of frequencies introducing a density that initiated this loss of connection to each other and the Cosmos? Would humanity have to wait for the next Golden Age for its next evolutionary leap or was this dark age and the inherent chaos the fertile ground that would push us through the dark birth canal, the eye of the needle into greater awareness and greater abilities? What would happen if we now consciously shifted our attention and awareness to the *Light Body?* Could we regain our telepathic, clairvoyant, clairsentient and clairaudient abilities, no longer merely accessible to the few, but that we as a tribe could once again claim them as more efficient forms of communication accessed beyond the speed of light?

She had landed in Madrid with a six-hour layover before boarding her flight to Lima. She'd been so deep in thought that she barely recalled landing and making her way across the concourse, but there she was seated at the departure gate for Lima. She needed to eat and locate an area where she could sleep for a couple hours. It would be nearly another sixteen hours before her arrival in Cusco, her final destination.

Reflections

Catherine had found her way back to her six-year-old self with her child's zeal and yearning to commune with Spirit. She'd lived her childhood with parents who hardly knew how to love themselves, let alone their children. The repeated woundings and abandonment over time had caused the light to dim and to fade; doubts had taken root and in her worst moments despair set in. Self-reliance had become her foundational belief. She had learned as a child not to ask for or count on help. She'd learned that to ask for help meant being admonished and ridiculed. The people closest to her, the family she'd relied on, were her greatest source of distress rather than the source of comfort and safety that a loving family might have provided. Yet these experiences would later become the means by which she would set herself free. Veil upon veil had to be removed; lies, deceits, deep-rooted beliefs and betrayals of her immediate past. Later she'd have to face thousands of years of conditioning she'd carried from lifetime to lifetime. The angst of facing her past drove her away from it. She'd turned her attention to becoming someone; on the surface, choosing not to be defined by her past.

The beautiful veneer she'd created brought her to her supervisors' attention; she had a quick mind, an ease with words and so she gained support for her advancement. While alone, she often felt empty and unfulfilled. She continued on this path until the prison that her success had created could no longer be ignored; she'd forgotten the way out. This loss of soul left her feeling vacant and at times listless. The work that at once brought her joy and defined her could no longer sustain her. She left her career abruptly much to the surprise of her colleagues. She packed her belongings and placed them in storage. Just days after her twenty-ninth birthday, she bought a one-way ticket to Rishikesh, India.

Once she arrived, she walked the streets of the town and found herself frequently peering into doorways where she heard the voices of people chanting. She would later learn that this is one aspect of Sadhana. Often, she stood at the back of the room looking in, yet exiting within moments. Then one morning in a part of town she'd newly discovered, she opened the door to a makeshift temple and was met by the gaze of a guru who sat at the front of the room. His eyes on the surface appeared dispassionate; yet the light shining through them let Catherine know that he had transcended all sorrow, all pain, all grasping, all aversion.

She stood at the end of the hall transfixed by his gaze. Eventually, she broke eye contact and found a seat on the floor among the yogis who swayed as they chanted accompanied by the yogini at the front of the room who played harmonium and led the call and response. She found herself opening to the beauty and abandon with which those present offered their beseeching and praises to God. She too began to sway; foreign words began to form and issue from her as she joined the chorus. After an hour the music came to a close. She felt an unnameable sense of peace as she sat in the silence following Satsang. She closed her eyes to shut out all distractions and savor the feeling. When she opened her eyes, many had made their departure. She got up and went through the door stepping into a brilliant day.

Vivid colors and fragrant, exotic scents greeted her as she walked toward the market stalls. Everything appeared more alive as if a veil had been removed and she needed to adjust to the emanating radiance; the sunlight reflecting off the water, the light moving and shifting with the breeze in the foliage of nearby trees. She had entered a superconscious state. She felt a rush of emotion she had not experienced for months. Joy. It was swiftly followed by sorrow and tears, both unexpected and overwhelming. There was no holding back the flood. As her sobs and tears subsided, she realized that her grief was for all the years lost. When had she closed her heart? How had she lived without feeling, steering toward what appeared safe and predictable and away from what was unconsciously surveyed as a dangerous shore? The visceral pain of allowing her heart to open brought more tears.

She returned to the temple every morning for months. She studied the Gita, the Upanishads, Patanjali and the Sutras.

She found, after a search, an English translation of the Yoga Aphorism of Patanjali. She carried it wherever she went, dog-earred and underlined. She listened intently to Gurudev's teachings which preceded Sadhana. Her meditation practice revealed her shadow side, all the dark and light stowed away in her deep unconscious asking to be seen and released. She learned to apprehend them with compassion. This emptying and purification gradually made room for more light, joy and buoyancy. Catherine could not remember when she had been so happy or felt so free.

℘

Catherine awoke before dawn and found her way to the terrace outside her room for morning meditation. For months she had longed to pierce the veil that would raise her to a new level of understanding. That morning she had let go of outcomes and surrendered to the stillness; she found herself slipping into an intensity of being that she could not nor wished to find words to describe. The early morning birdsong, the fly on her skin, the scent of the flowers, the trees existed within her, all life forms right down to the microbiota innately and intimately a part of her. There was a dawning, a sudden apprehension that over millennia her awareness had expressed itself in a myriad of forms and that all lived within her. Her sense of separation dissolved.

During the days that followed, as she walked the streets, she could glance at a passerby and know what *medicine* was

needed. A veil had lifted. She wondered if it would be temporary and if she could sustain it; if so, what was needed on
her part? She felt a new sense of responsibility, a new understanding that everything that lives and has form, animate
or inanimate, was sacred and intelligent. Each was charged
with a role to play to maintain a balance. She wondered how
humans got so off course. She was being presented with an
opportunity to adjust her trajectory. Could she be still and
listen, really listen? Could she humble herself and choose to
act from a greater awareness?

Deep within, she'd known this for a long time, but the
pull of the world had distorted her vision and had supported
the dichotomy of form and spirit. What had been revealed
was the inseparable nature of matter from spirit. How had
she sustained this disparity for so long? Had it not cost her
massive amounts of energy to maintain this separation? The
old structures now appeared flimsy and false. And yet they
had seemed so concrete and impenetrable.

After eighteen months in India, her life had shifted radically. The time had come to return to the States. She would
not be returning to New York to her career as a fashion
magazine editor. She would return to the family farm. Keeping
the farm operating had been a struggle for as long as Catherine
could remember. Her father had not been suited to the task
of maintaining a farm. Her brothers had left for the cities as
soon as they could. Enforced labor and their father's tongue
lashings had left them with little interest in staying on.

When Catherine returned, her father had been gone for nearly ten years. Her mother's health was failing and she had rented the pastures and fields to neighboring farmers for several years now. She had arrived without any intention of staying let alone assuming responsibility for the farm. But she saw everything with new eyes and the expanse and beauty of the land, the ponds, the sugar bush and the 300-year-old stand of oaks captured her heart.

When her mother passed, the land passed on to her. She'd already reclaimed many areas that had lain fallow for many years. The leases with neighboring farms were terminated. She'd purchased a herd of sheep and mohair goats and implemented the early stages of her experiments with biodynamic farming. She became intimately acquainted with every square inch of the two-hundred-and-fifty-acre farm. Some areas brought up childhood memories, places where she'd escaped to when the atmosphere at home became threatening. The wildflowers, trees and open spaces had helped her to return to a state of calm.

Nearly five years after her return, she met Francis one late fall evening at a lecture given by a professor of Ethnobiology at a nearby college. He sat in the row behind her and followed her out after the lecture. They fell into easy conversation moving from one topic to another. He was delighted to discover that she was the owner of the farm he drove by nearly every day on his way to his university teaching position. He'd watched the transformation that had taken place the last few years and wondered if new owners had purchased the land. He was surprised to learn that Catherine's family had owned the land for several generations and had gone through cycles of prosperity and decline. He admired her ambition, her courage to go it alone. He taught physics veering off into the recently introduced field of quantum physics as an addendum to the traditional mechanical model stipulated by the academic schedule. His digressions from the curriculum were tolerated because of his academic record and the enthusiasm he incited in his students.

Francis and Catherine married the following year. Francis had sold his place in the neighboring town and moved to the farm. Within months Catherine was expecting; Fynn was born in the spring. Francis was an academic and would always remain so. He had a great interest in the farm but he remained superficially involved with the running of it; that was Catherine's ever-growing domain. Having married at fifty, becoming a father was rather unexpected. He took great delight in his responsibilities as a father; in fact, he assumed much of his son's care for the first few months as spring and the growing season were soon underway following Fynn's arrival. Catherine had not expected the unassuming way that Francis had stepped in to be of assistance in any way he could. He prepared evening meals and assumed other domestic duties without hesitation anticipating what needed attention. He took a year's sabbatical from the university and devoted his free time to his research. Freed of these domestic responsibilities, Catherine was able to devote more time to being a mother and attending to the demands of the farm.

Francis did not share Catherine's passion for Eastern spirituality but he always remained curious and interested. Through lengthy discussions, they found a bridge to cross the divide of science and spirituality. The latest discoveries in the quantum world were presenting new ways of entertaining reality that pointed to common principles. Each had a unique lexicon, and when examined discreetly, both seemed to be pointing to the same conclusions. Their discussions presented fresh ways of seeing that shed light on these supposedly divergent disciplines. They often spent the last hours of the day together, casually discussing their latest insights and discoveries or reading quietly stretched out on the sofa or out on the porch swing.

Catherine devoted the winter months to in-depth studies in biodynamics and the little-known agricultural practices of indigenous cultures. In the spring there would be test plots and areas devoted to what seemed worthy of investigation and implementation. Fynn in tow, Catherine surveyed the farm looking for ways to support greater biodiversity and to implement practices that insured fertility and sustainability. Her innovative ideas got the attention of several faculty members at the nearby university's agricultural school. She was invited to lecture and eventually established an internship program at the farm. The farm was productive, innovative and successful. Her staff grew to accommodate its expansion.

Fynn admired his mother's industrious nature and love of innovation, but much like his father, he was drawn to academia. His area of study was anthropology which after university led to digs and research projects in Africa, Australia and South America. His extensive field studies and discoveries eventually led to a university position on the East coast. Fynn met Olivia, an adjunct professor in the school of the Arts, soon after her arrival from Rhode Island. She was an art historian; social, extraverted and animated. She loved music and dance and had great fashion sense. Fynn was immediately drawn to her spontaneity and love of beauty. They married and settled in New England. Their visits to the farm were infrequent but always relaxed and enjoyable, both Fynn and Olivia losing themselves to the carefree atmosphere of rural life and Catherine's farm.

During a summer visit, they announced that Olivia was expecting. Lilly was born and shifted their lives away from careers and toward family. To Catherine's delight, their visits became more frequent and they stayed longer. Then, quite unexpectedly, Fynn was gone. He'd been struck by an oncoming vehicle that had crossed the median late one night as he was returning from a speaking engagement. Olivia was prone to anxiety, a result of losing her mother when she was eight. She always feared that those she loved most could disappear without warning. Fynn's death was devastating. She became immobilized, unable to move forward. Olivia's father and Catherine offered support. Catherine spent several weeks after the funeral helping out. She attended to Lilly's needs providing a caring presence for her granddaughter to express her grief at the loss of her father and her growing anxiety as she watched her mother retreat from life.

Francis had quietly passed away at home three years before Fynn's death. Catherine had seen it coming for months, as he retreated further into himself as his life energy began to ebb. They had found a way to say goodbye, express their gratitude for their long journey together and allow for Francis' release. Catherine awoke one morning to find that he had gone during the night.

She returned to the farm after weeks in Amherst, her heart heavy with grief; she would survive the loss of her son. Fynn had left this physical plane but she sensed his presence. Her grief extended to those left behind, Olivia and Lilly. She prayed that with time Olivia would move beyond this painful loss and that she could turn to Lilly and find comfort and a reason to move forward.

The years that followed were rejuvenating. Catherine offered safety and guidance when Lilly arrived. Lilly's moods were unpredictable as she experienced intense feelings of anger, rejection and loss. Catherine knew the importance of allowing for this process and release. It would take its own course and dissipate in its own time.

Life unfolded in relative ease and Catherine watched with joy as Lilly demonstrated her passion for the land and for its stewardship. Once Lilly returned from her studies and travels,

Catherine turned the farm over to her. Another expansion was underway with Lilly's vision setting the direction going forward. Catherine took great pleasure in watching new methods being introduced and projects taking form. Students brought novel ideas and Lilly seemed to thrive as an academic fixed on implementation lending support to untried ideas and encouraging experimentation. The farm took on a new name, *Rare Earth*.

Langston's sudden death had brought a time of sorrow that Catherine felt deeply. The family had been shaken, its resilience tested. In time, life beckoned them and they answered the call. Lilly did not turn from her grief; instead, she turned toward it for all that it had to teach her about love and impermanence.

The loss of Langston led to Lilly's redoubled efforts to share her vision: nature's fundamental principles of cooperation and unbridled participation as the foundation upon which all of life unfolds, evolves and thrives; a multi-storied complex system that at once creates profusion and self-regulation. Here lay wisdom mirrored extravagantly in ingenious and inexhaustible forms, a wordless primer expressing the intimate connection between nature and the unseen dimensions of reality.

Peaceful and rewarding years followed as Julia grew from childhood to adulthood with the same insatiable curiosity that dominated Catherine's and Lilly's spirits. Julia was intrepid and ambitious, tireless in her pursuits.

The years had moved swiftly, filled with contentment. Now at one hundred and four, Catherine felt her energy ebbing. She slipped into sleep more frequently and her desire for activity had waned considerably these past few months. She was waiting for Lilly and Julia's return from South America. Then she could go.

Machu Picchu

Lilly watched, her heart swelling, as her disheveled daughter made her way down the concourse and toward her, Julia raising her hand as they made eye contact, obviously tired but filled with excitement at their anticipated reunion. Their long embrace made them both appreciate how much they had missed each other's company these past fifteen months. The wait had been long while Julia had queued customs and security. At last, they made it down to baggage claim. Julia had not had a solid meal in nearly twenty-four hours so their next destination was the little cafe on Centro Tinku that Lilly had discovered on a previous visit. It featured French and South American cuisine.

Lilly remembered the covered terrace and open-air tables in a pretty courtyard with lovely French music in the background. An outdoor setting seemed very fitting after countless hours in an enclosed air cabin. Sunday brunch would be lovely and help them land, welcoming terra firma. They could follow with showers and naps at the inn near Centro Historico where Lilly had rented rooms for Julia, Drew and herself. Cusco was a great place to recover from a long journey and they would have the next couple days to explore the city.

The food arrived; Julia had ordered a cream soup for starters that had been delicately seasoned with a hint of saffron seeping through the potato, corn and pea foundation; the garnish was barely-wilted pea shoots. She followed the first course with chicken crepes. Lilly selected Huevos Rancheros with guacamole and beans that were well seasoned and beautifully presented. For dessert, they both selected a flaky pastry with seasonal fruit. The food had replenished and sedated them. Both wondered if they had the energy to make it back to the inn on foot. They lingered over coffee quietly enjoying each other's presence and eventually hailed a cab.

Drew would arrive later that afternoon. They would explore the city; take in the San Pedro Market, the Plaza de Armas, the Cusco Cathedral and the Museo Inka. The cacao factory tour was on Julia's *Places to Visit* list with its delectable tasting opportunities. Their shop offered wonderful delicacies which at first seemed pricey, but given that this business worked with allied communities that paid fair prices from locally sourced ingredients, Julia did not object. It was a way to make a contribution to the knowledge exchange that took place between grower and producer. Lilly was thinking of the many Peruvian restaurants with five-star ratings in Cusco and thought that the next couple days could turn into an eating extravaganza. Both were sure that Drew, having been in Peru for the past three years, would have ideas of his own on what and where.

They met Drew at the train station late in the afternoon. Julia and Drew had not been together since he left the farm.

Twelve years had gone by and both marveled at the changes in appearance that had transpired during that time. Julia's hair was long, her jaw and cheekbones more pronounced in her late twenties. Drew sported a short-cropped beard, dark blond hair and a sinewy frame, the result of the rugged environment, the physical work of farming and village life. Julia was somewhat surprised at the rush of emotion that came over her as they exchanged greetings and hugs.

Lilly had maintained a relationship with Drew and a great interest in his projects since he had left the farm. She had raised money to support the *Meraki Project* at its inception and had seen video footage of the various projects and phases of development over the past three years but this would be her first visit to the village. Julia had often turned to Drew for inspiration when she felt stymied. They'd corresponded frequently during her recent travels, emails and texts whenever possible. Emotions ran high as everyone expressed their excitement at this long-awaited reunion. They headed for the inn to drop off Drew's bags and then met up at the bar off the inn's lobby for a glass of South American wine before making plans for dinner.

The conversation was lively, each taking turns elaborating on the details of their travels and projects. Eventually the conversation turned to Catherine. Drew and Catherine had forged a lasting friendship over the years. Lilly was sad to share that she had slowed down considerably these past few months, and sensed Catherine was ready to leave this world soon. Julia's eyes teared up. She'd known the day would come when her great-grandmother would make her departure – her soul sister, her mentor, the wise one. She'd been gifted many years of her tutelage and countless hours in her company and her abiding love. She cherished every moment; her departure would create a great void, one no one else could fill. Julia became aware that the mood had shifted. She saw that both Drew and Lilly had drifted from the conversation, both no doubt filled with sorrow at the thought of Catherine's passing. Julia suddenly suggested that perhaps they should consider dinner plans. Within minutes they came to an agreement as to where to dine this evening. They left and fell into easy conversation as the mood slowly lifted. Drew had suggested a Peruvian restaurant he had discovered a couple years ago. It was located on Calle Arequipa. He recalled delicious food and excellent service.

They were greeted with *amuse-bouche,* a bite-size appetizer, along with a taste of Chica as soon as they were seated. All three selected dishes with the intention of sharing and experiencing as many tastes as possible. They sampled *Ensalada de Nuestro Huerto,* a hand-picked selection of the freshest in-season vegetables, *Ensalada de Quinua,* quinoa, baked apples, Paria cheese, lettuce and confit tomatoes, *Patasca Soup,* a Peruvian specialty. For the main course, they selected *Pollito Chacrero,* crispy and tender chicken, cooked on stones, seasoned with Andean herbs served with oven-roasted potatoes; *Crocante de Trucha,* a trout fillet in quinoa crust served with grilled vegetables; *Arroz Chaufu Amazonico,* Amazonian fried rice with sauteed pork jerky, chorizo, chicken, plantain and quail eggs. Their incredibly friendly and knowledgeable server suggested wine pairings to accompany their food selections. The atmosphere was friendly and welcoming, the food was delicious, and the presentations were beautiful. They finished the meal sharing a rich chocolate pudding.

As they walked out two hours later, a bit giddy from the wine, the company and long travels, each welcomed the night air and the walk back to the inn. The mood was subdued as they eased effortlessly into the quiet that follows a day of excitement and animated conversations.

❧

The next morning Julia woke up feeling disoriented. Her dream time travels had taken her to a strange place accompanied by what would in ordinary reality seem like impossible feats. She was attending a social gathering of close friends. They sat around a fire engaged in conversation, the atmosphere relaxed. Three new guests suddenly appeared out of the darkness, none of them familiar to Julia. There was something different about them. When Julia looked at them from her peripheral vision, they each appeared to have a luminescent aura surrounding them. As soon as she looked at them directly, the light disappeared. They listened attentively as the conversation resumed and in time joined in. As each spoke Julia could see a bright light emanating from the solar plexus. It seemed as if no one else in the group was aware of this. As soon as they became silent, the light would fade, almost disappearing. She'd never met them before; she wondered who had invited them. They seemed relaxed and at ease. Nothing about their physical appearance would indicate this curious phenomenon. Why was she the only one who was aware of it? Were her friends also witnessing this? She looked around the group hoping to make eye contact to confirm her suspicions. Her silent inquiry was noticed by the newcomers and they turned their attention to her and initiated telepathic communication. She could hardly believe it! Why had she been singled out? Suddenly, it was as if the entire gathering had disappeared and she and the three strangers were the only ones present. What followed was a wordless transmission of information. The speed with which it was delivered made it impossible for Julia to absorb it cognitively. The volume of information being conveyed was staggering. Julia suddenly felt overwhelmed causing her to surface, startled out of sleep; she was back in her room at the inn. The dream lingered and stayed with her throughout the day, seeping through her wakeful hours, her visit to the museum and her time with Drew and her mother. In the months that followed she would access the information transmitted as an intuitive stream in sudden and unexpected flashes.

The next day, after a light breakfast at the inn, Lilly, Drew and Julia made their way to the Museo Inka. The building rests on Inca foundations; artifacts from Inca and Pre-Inca times fill several floors and multiple rooms. The Pre-Inca collections include information and artifacts on Andean Hunter-Gatherers, ceramic pieces that date back as far as 5000 BC. They saw displays of ancient water holders, bowls, ceremonial items and rock sculptures. Lilly was intrigued by the metal and gold work, the jewelry and textiles and the ceremonial Inca drinking vessels fashioned from wood. Drew was drawn to the display of decorated shells used by the Incas as trumpets. The Incas enjoyed festivals and music; Drew was reminded of the villagers and their love of celebration and singing, a tradition that persisted in Andean culture to this day.

Julia was intrigued by the Ancient Inca architecture techniques, evidence of which she found on the streets of Cusco in buildings and construction. Ashlar, blocks of stone, were cut to fit together tightly without mortar, an unsurpassed engineering feat that pointed to the Inca's superior understanding of physics and mathematics. Another construction method was called *pillow-faced* architecture, the finally shaped stones fitting in jigsaw like patterns. Ashlar masonry was reserved for the most sacred Inca structures.

Julia had made her way to photos of the ruins of the Chincero Estate. She was engrossed by the captions below the photos which revealed that the *Sapa Inca*, the ruler of the Inca Empire, believed that the beauty, the aesthetic appeal of the palace rested on and reflected a mutual relationship between the Inca's imperial power and that of the earth itself, what they believed to be spiritual authority. She was struck by the words as they implied that there was an inherent power to a structure when constructed consciously and intentionally, principles she had learned in her studies of Vedic Architecture.

Scholars believed that the Inca had inherited *caninacukpirca*, dry fitted masonry, from Tiwanaku, founded in the second century BC. It is characterized by its use of the natural environment; buildings slightly inclined and the corners rounded. The natural bedrock becomes part of the foundation to keep the building stable and create seismic resistance. This architectural style uses the topography and materials of the land as part of the design shaping stones to conceal natural outcrops or fit to crevices. What seemed extraordinary to Julia was their vision and execution of merging their architecture with the land. She found herself anticipating her time in Machu Picchu. She felt inspired. Everything she learned in the past decade about ancient and contemporary architecture that was rooted in the earth could be synthesized and defined her vision for the future.

The Museo had an extensive collection and after three hours they had reached their saturation point. They left the museum and agreed on a place for lunch. The afternoon was devoted to the chocolate factory. Julia knew that with some probing on her end, she would gain some insights on economic collaboration, an important aspect of her ambitious project.

They arrived and were welcomed with cups of *Chililique*, a chocolate elixir, so named for the village in Northern Peru, a rich drinking chocolate seasoned with native herbs, flowers and chilis. The factory tour began with video footage of the harvest, followed by the fermentation process, the beans being bagged and shipped to various destinations. The tour guide shared valuable information about *panela,* an organic unrefined sugar, providing details about its multi-step production and its use in their cacao products. She explained that the artisanal process employed to produce *panela* maintains its nutrients, minerals, vitamins and proteins.

She then spoke of the small village in the Ecuadorian Andes where they source their milk. The cows are milked by hand and pasture raised. She spoke of the code of sustainable practices the cooperative established with their partners from Peru, Ecuador and Columbia. She elaborated on their safe labor practices, their commitment to human rights and upholding environmentally friendly practices.

As she spoke, she walked them through the process of mechanically removing the shells. Graduated mesh screens ensure that the beans are shell-free before the cacao nibs are ground to a cacao mass. The mass is heated creating a chocolate liquor and then processed into two components, cacao solids and cacao butter. These are conveyed to the blending area where recipes and ratios are meticulously maintained with precise measurements and the addition of herbs, flowers and spices sourced for quality, freshness and impeccability. Tempering is the final step and provides proper texture and appearance. Chocolate tempering machines with computer controls assure consistent results.

Julia, Drew and Lilly left the tour and headed to the confectionery adjacent to the factory to purchase truffles. The problem was what to choose; there were so many delicious and exotic options.

Their next destination was the Botanical Garden of the Plaza San Francisco. These gardens hold a collection of native plants of the Andes which have medicinal properties. The trees, shrubs and plants are labeled with detailed information along with the plants' common and scientific names. Drew became their unofficial tour guide as he was familiar with some of the plants having learned them from the villagers in the mountains. The variety of plants was extensive; the central attraction for most visitors was the Q'antu, considered the national flower of Peru and also known as the flower of the Inca. These tall evergreen shrubs were evident throughout the park with their distinctive clusters of elongated bell flowers. The first they came to displayed bright pink flowers. Drew was sharing that in veneration of the *Apus,* the sacred mountains, Q'antu also called Cantuta flowers are placed on their slopes expressing respect and appreciation. Considered a ceremonial flower, the Inca would carpet the path with these flowers as a sign of respect for the one honored in ritual.

Next, they strolled over to the Quena shrub, an evergreen with small leaves and large amounts of dead twigs. It is revered for its shedding multi-layered bark that helps the earth to remain fertile. Drew then pointed out the Hawanq'ollay Giganton, a plant the women of the village used to wash wool.

As they left the park, the conversation turned to trees. Drew shared his findings on the tree reclamation project that had occupied a better part of the past three years in the village. Once the village's basic needs had been met and a way to create a financial future was established, Drew and the villagers had turned their energies to reforestation. Already, Drew could see the benefits. The cover of trees slowed erosion, and as they grew toward maturity, they would buffer wind and affect the climate, including rainfall. The benefit to the villagers was most apparent. Having lived surrounded by trees, the clearcutting and the way it had been managed had deeply affected the villagers. Gone was the protection the trees and the forest spirits offered. Drew explained that their relationship with trees went beyond utility and was informed by a deep reverence for the forest. It provides shelter, fire, medicine and wisdom.

As the forest was reestablished Drew had participated in frequent ceremonies and rituals offered to the forest expressing gratitude and asking for forgiveness. The village Shaman had often spoken of the necessity to reestablish a connection with the forest spirits asking them to return to support the health and wellbeing of the village.

Drew spoke of the complex world that exists in the tree canopies of the forest; teeming with diversity, the canopies feed an incomprehensible variety of wildlife and invisible species such as fungi, molds and bacteria. Drew's concern was that this rich biodiversity had been destroyed with the extent of clearcutting.

Could it be recreated as the forest matured and was allowed to evolve naturally? They were creating a mixed native forest of densely planted trees, shrubs and vegetation recreated with understory species closely mimicking what would be a naturally occurring network of trees, shrubs and plants of different heights whose requirements would naturally be provided for.

The topic of trees took them well into dinner and the remaining evening. Lilly spoke of the extensive research which had been carried out by a handful of scientists with a passion for trees. Tree research has been sparse and the forest ecosystem is poorly understood. All three understood the unseen benefits of spending time in the woods, but these benefits were now being carefully studied and the results were astounding. Lilly was reflecting on her times spent in the evergreen woods on the northern end of the farm, and the scent of the woods rose in her memory, this sudden recall eliciting a relaxation response.

She talked about the studies that were showing that people who spent time among trees had lower concentrations of cortisol, lower blood pressure, lower pulse rates and greater parasympathetic response. The study of tree aerosols was also showing that plant hormones and other natural chemical mists in minute doses become available to flora, fauna and visitors alike that were proving to have measurable antibiotic, antiviral and anticancer properties. Initial studies indicated that these chemicals appeared to be highly effective in small concentrations.

She shared the details of Langston's research years ago. He had been involved in a project that used trees to remediate water pollution problems. Trees had the ability to take up toxic waste, to neutralize and metabolize it. It was a technique known as *phytoremediation*. The researchers had found that willows and poplars were particularly effective for the removal of toxic wastes, what is now considered a valuable form of ecotechnology.

Drew brought the conversation around to the Druids, the high priests of the Celts; they taught that rocks, clouds, each tree, each mountain were sacred and held mystical power, that each offered a way to connect with the Divine. The native culture of the Celts was embedded in the forest. It was a source of food, inspiration and medicine.

Julia wondered about a world where a person's intentions, feelings and actions contributed to either its greater good and to its failure. She marveled at having discovered yet another example of an ancient culture who understood and whose very foundations rested on these sacred truths, teaching both veneration for the world we inhabit and individual responsibility for the whole, from the microcosm to the macrocosm. Wasn't modern science now rediscovering these same principles at work in the multiverse, she reflected.

Julia's attention turned back to the conversation and wondered if she should share the details of her final shamanic journey in Siberia. She knew that Siberian Shamans believed that trees were intercessors between earth and sky. She would wait for another opportunity. It was getting late and they would be leaving for Ollanta in the morning. Excitement ran high as they headed for their rooms to pack and rest. The journey to Machu Picchu was upon them.

Morning came and they packed the car for an early departure. They had elected to drive to Ollantaytambo, a two-hour journey crossing the beautiful landscape of the Sacred Valley of the Incas. In Ollanta, so called by the locals, they would spend the remainder of the day exploring the Inca Ceremonial Center, *Carro Bandolista* and take in the valleys of Urubamba covered by extensive agricultural terraces. Drew was interested in visiting the storehouses, the *qiloqa,* built out of field stones from the surrounding hills. The storehouses featured a ventilation system to protect their content, speculated to be mainly grain.

They had reserved rooms at a local guesthouse and the plaza offered a variety of eateries devoted to western tourists with a few Peruvian offerings. In the morning, they would make their way to the train station and make the short journey to Aguas Calientes.

∾

The Plaza was alive with vendors and tourists haggling over prices when they first arrived. They made their way to Mercado San Pedro. They purchased fruits, drinks and snacks and sat on benches in the shade sharing food and watching the comings and goings of the newly arrived tourists, most here for only a night either destined for or returning from

Machu Picchu. It was a beautiful sunny day; the sky brilliant and cloudless, the sun selflessly pouring golden light on the mountains, the marketplace and passerbys coloring everything with warmth and beauty.

As evening arrived Julia, Lilly and Drew gathered in the courtyard outside their adjoining rooms. The walls surrounding the courtyard were covered with lush vines and pale colored blossoms, the profusion of flowers exuding a sweet exotic scent in the cool evening air. Drew started a fire in the primitive fire pit in the center of the courtyard.

Lilly had stepped back into her room and soon returned with *Mapacho* tobacco. A small ceremony seemed appropriate before their morning departure for the Inca Citadel. Lilly initiated the ceremony and began with a request from *Mapacho* to remove all obstacles, both seen and unseen, as they embarked on their journey. She humbly requested that the spirits of this sacred place welcome them and bestow their wisdom upon them. She asked for guidance that each may receive what was most needed to stay true to their vision to honor and assist Gaia in her healing and evolution. They were aware that this was a sacred pilgrimage, that they were traveling to a powerful place and that preparation was needed when connecting with the Sacred Apu. Most who traveled to Machu Picchu were there to explore ancient Inca culture, a few came to experience the power that dwells there. Drew considered it a temple to honor the sacred mountain. He saw it as one of the crown chakras of the world.

That night Lilly dreamed of Langston. He had come to her over the years bringing comfort and messages that had supported her especially in the early years following his death. His visitations became fewer over time but were always welcomed even if they brought with them a lingering melancholy. That night, he smiled and told her, *It's time.*

When she awoke, she sensed he would not come again. She had experienced a shift these past couple years; she was ready to create a life with someone. She was also ready to wind down her research and devote more time to her personal life. She was slowly turning over the responsibilities of the farm to the people who had proved to be reliable and dedicated contributors, those who had been with her for many years and shared her passion and her vision. She was confident in their abilities and would remain active in decision making and long-range planning.

Drew and Julia lingered by the fire after Lilly went to bed. Both had looked forward to their reunion after more than a decade; neither was prepared for the mutual attraction which became more apparent as the days went by. Both had shared their deepest motivations for their work, what inspired them and informed their way of life, all that they still planned to create.

They'd eventually wandered into Julia's room as the fire died down and the evening cooled. The conversation had taken on a more personal tone. After a time, they'd fallen asleep on Julia's bed holding each other until close to dawn. Drew woke up abruptly realizing they had overslept and

Lilly would soon be wondering where they were. He sat up and stirred Julia to wakefulness. She immediately leaped into action gathering the last of her belongings. Drew left for his room, and Julia packed as she moved through a tangle of dissonant reflections as her mind drifted to the previous hours with Drew. She took in a deep breath and found a way to quiet her mind and listen with her heart. There would be time for reflection; now was not the time.

They barely made it to the station in time to board the train. Lilly was puzzled by their tardiness assuming the excitement of the day ahead would have meant rising early for both of them. The views from the train were spectacular; the photos and information they'd looked at and shared were hardly a match for the actual beauty of the Sacred Valley of the Incas.

They arrived in Aguas Caliente and made their way to the buses that would take them to Machu Picchu. The bus ride over steep inclines and dramatic views of mountains and valleys were a preview of what awaited them once they reached their destination. The bus moved through mist and clouds and the terrain was green and lush. As they stepped off the bus, the sheer drops and steep surrounding peaks were witnessed against the mighty roaring river hundreds of feet below, the river bending and embracing Machu Picchu above on three sides. The power, the wisdom and the ancient knowledge was palpable and seemed entwined with the spirit of the land. The ashlar construction and the configurations based on astrology

– the solstice, the equinox and celestial alignments added to the sacred aura of the place.

The temples are situated in the upper town. The western section of the town is separated from the east by the square and was designated for ceremonial and religious purposes. Here they found the *Torre'on,* the Temple of the Sun, a semicircular temple designed for rituals celebrating seasonal celestial events. Carved from the rock foundation of the temple were two large basins; it was surmised that these were filled with water and used as mirrors to observe the skies. The Serpent's Door facing north opens onto a series of sixteen pools commanding a great view of Huayna Picchu. They then made their way to *Intihuatana,* a ritual stone that was common in Inca culture. It was placed so that it would be in direct alignment with the sun on the winter solstice. The Incas believed that the *Intihuatana* held the sun in its annual path in the sky.

They then found the entrance to Inti Mach'ay, the cave where the Royal Feast of the Sun took place. Julia paused to take in the impressive masonry of the walls, steps and windows of the cave. The festival was held in December concluding on the Winter Solstice, the day noble boys were initiated into manhood.

Lilly had made her way to the Room of the Three Windows on her own. She'd been particularly drawn to this site. The large open room features three massive windows of trapezoidal construction. She found herself drawn to the windows. She stood before the central window looking off into the distance; she suddenly experienced a shudder. It was as if a strong gust of wind had suddenly created a ripple in the fabric of what she saw, throwing her off balance. The edges of her vision rippled as if observing a scene reflected in water, the water so still as to be impossible to distinguish between the reflection and the objects reflected. She turned her gaze and saw Julia and Drew approaching. A roaring sound seemed to take over, guiding her attention back to the window. The sound and its frequency became so powerful she doubted her ability to remain standing. As she gazed through the window, the mountains disappeared; what she saw before her were lights and ghostly images. They seemed plausible and almost familiar. She felt as if she entered a new dimension, a fresh reference point, a potential yet to be. A viewing of what might yet be? Her vision ended abruptly, brought back to current time as she felt Julia's hand on her arm asking her *Mom, are you OK? Where did you go; you seemed so far away.* Unable to find words, she squeezed her daughter's hand.

They had spent an inordinate amount of time exploring everything of interest to each of them, delaying their departure until the last bus leaving at dusk. Reflecting on the ride back to Aguas Calientes, what had been most unexpected for all of them was the culture of the Incas. They were intrigued by the *Amawtakuna*, the philosopher-scholars who educated the upper classes and the residences of *Amautas*, the wise persons, whose homes were characterized by reddish walls.

The *Amawtakuna* constituted a special class of wise men. They included philosophers, poets and priests who kept the knowledge of the Incas alive. They imparted their knowledge of their culture and traditions throughout their realm. Being highly educated, they were charged with the responsibility of educating those of royal blood. This form of specialized education was extended to members of conquered cultures for those who held administrative roles. The language of the empire was highly promoted.

Drew and Julia were fascinated by the use of *Quipus,* the word for knot; It appeared to be a little-known or understood method of record-keeping and communication introduced by the *Amawtakuna.* At first glance, the system seemed, to both Julia and Drew, to mimic a binary system. And yet it dates back to an ancient civilization. Time lines seemed to blur and disappear between what was and what is as they delved deeper and gained more information.

Quipus were recording devices created from strings. The cords stored numeric as well as other values encoded as knots. A *quipu* could have thousands of cords, their configurations resembling string maps. At times, finely carved wood was used as a base to which color-coded strings were attached. One researcher speculated that *quipus* were a system of representational symbols, much like numerals or music notation. They convey information but are not related to sounds associated with speech and language.

℘

On their return to Ollanta, they settled into their former rooms. It had been a long day but Julia wanted to check in with her mother. She wondered about Lilly's experience in the Room with Three Windows. She sensed her mother had been shaken by what had occurred. Perhaps it was too soon and Lilly would not be ready to discuss what had transpired while standing in the opening of the massive central window. Julia made her way to Lilly's room; on entering she sensed her mother was deep in thought. Julia ventured a few words of concern to which Lilly responded in a dismissive and reassuring way. Julia relaxed into acceptance knowing her mother would open up in her own time.

The Return Journey

They decided to make the return trip to Cusco by train. Once they were settled in, at Drew's prompting, Julia began to recount her time in Turkey. She had traveled to Istanbul specifically to witness a performance of the Whirling Dervishes. She had sat mesmerized as the dancers were hypnotically transported by repetitive motion, circling to an inner destination fluidly and soundlessly moving.

Julia had traveled to Turkey with clear intentions. She had timed her arrival in Istanbul so she could purchase a ticket for the Sunday performance. It was held in an intimate setting, a restored Ottoman Turkish bath with limited seating, the event witnessed by visitors who must keep in mind that it is a religious ceremony.

Julia had been fascinated by the Whirling Dervishes since childhood. Catherine had read Rumi's poetry and explained that the Mevlevi Order of the Sufis had been founded by his followers in the thirteenth century shortly after his death. Rumi, a mystical Sufi master, believed that through chants, prayers, music and dance one could establish a close relationship with God.

Whirling was considered a mystical journey and a symbolic imitation of planets orbiting the sun, a dance performed as a ritual. Sufis seek to find God, Divine Love through a direct and personal experience. The *semazen's* clothing and the movement of the dance are replete with symbolism. The dance is considered a meditation. The dancers' movements, graceful and hypnotic, are performed with the intention of releasing the ego and represent man's rise toward love and perfection. The Persian music assisted both dancer and viewer in entering another realm.

Afterwards, she'd walked the streets drifting, still under the spell of the ceremony; she found herself in an art district. She abruptly came to a stop before the canvases in a gallery window. They depicted whirling dervishes emerging from wine goblets, swirling and rising from the wine. She recalled Rumi's many references to wine as a symbol conveying the soul's journey from earthly regions to the realm of the Divine. The gallery was closed but she longed to know who had been inspired to represent the dissolving of the self and its merging with the soul so beautifully. Julia's recollections were so vivid that Drew felt as though he had been there with her; especially the paintings she had described. He could visualize the pale-yellow background, the rosy color of the wine swirling in a splash up the side of the goblets and the *Semazen*, arms rising, emerging from the center of the ruby elixir.

The next day she had taken a train to Konya to visit Rumi's grave. She'd been taken aback by the bright turquoise dome as she approached the Mevlana Museum. It was difficult to find words to describe the richness of the mausoleum and do it justice. The sarcophagus located under the green dome was lavishly covered with brocade embroidered with verses of the Koran.

The Sultan who had invited Rumi to Konya had offered his rose garden for the burial of Rumi's father. When Rumi died, he was buried next to his father. Rumi's successor initiated the construction of the mausoleum in honor of the great Master; the burial chamber is located just below it. The surrounding rooms hold prayer rugs, dervish cloths, rare books and instruments used during the *Sema*. When Julia left the museum, she felt gratitude for all of Persia; despite the passage of centuries, Persia still held Rumi with deep esteem.

ॐ

Back in Ollanta, they elected to spend a couple days here. Drew wanted to gather supplies not easily available in the high Andes before their departure for the village. Drew was looking forward to their mountain journey; he was eager to share his village life and the transformation that had taken place over the past three years. He told them that Paco would be coming during their visit, that their collaborative venture had continued. He would be bringing a group of young people who would be staying for the next three months to work with the goats and assist with the forest project. In turn, he would head back to the Amazon basin with a group of young men and women from the village who would be taught the ancient ways, how to maintain soil fertility in a tropical climate with the use of *terra petra.*

Lilly noticed that a change had taken place between Drew and her daughter. Julia seemed to light up whenever Drew entered the room. She had noticed Julia's reaction when they first met up with Drew at the train station in Cusco but had dismissed it. They were spending considerably more time together since their return from Machu Picchu, frequently engaged in lively conversation. Julia had spontaneously asked if she could join Drew on his errands and he'd said yes. Lilly would have the afternoon to herself. She would explore Ollanta, looking for the town's quiet undiscovered places, those that reveal the character of the town beyond the reach of tourists.

∽

The journey to the village was tiring and long. They'd started out by train and then by bus on roads that were uneven and narrow. They moved slowly and the air grew cooler as they went up in elevation. Lilly and Julia sensed they were nearing their destination as Drew became more animated. Leaving the bus, they were met by a few village boys who had brought carts for the supplies Drew had purchased. A dilapidated truck awaited them for the rest of the journey, the village just a few miles away.

As they entered the village, they were greeted by the villagers who had been eagerly waiting for their arrival. The great affection they felt for Drew was immediately apparent to Lilly and Julia. On entering the village center, he was surrounded by young children each vying for attention. The women and men greeted him warm-heartedly and then turned their attention to his visitors. Lilly and Julia were greeted with a mixture of innocence and shyness, hands extended in welcome.

The scent of roasted meat and simmering pots reached them, carried on the late afternoon breeze. The villagers had been preparing for their arrival – the arrival of visitors was cause for a celebration. In the center of the village square stood a newly erected pavilion. Garlands of early spring flowers had been wrapped around the pillars in serpentine fashion. Low tables and cushions were sheltered under the cover of the pavilion. Everyone would be seated here and the area extended beyond its perimeter once the food was ready.

Lilly and Julia were escorted to a small one room house where they would stay during their visit. It was clear that someone had gone to great lengths to make them feel welcome. The room was sparsely furnished; a small wooden table and two chairs sat under a south-facing window. A bouquet of wildflowers had been placed in an earthenware vase that sat on the table. The whitewashed floorboards had been scrubbed and the room held several woven rugs of different sizes and colors.

The room was well lit as the windows had been situated to take advantage of the sun's changing path through the seasons. Two small twin beds had been made up and covered with brightly colored handwoven woolen blankets. A chair sat between the beds on which an oil lamp had been placed.

A small area of the room had been designated for quiet reflection and included a small altar. Two handmade cushions had been placed over the small rug in front of the altar. The altar consisted of a low wooden table that had been covered with a woven fabric of bright vermilion, indigo and yellow fashioned in a geometric pattern. The altar held a candle, some *palo santo*, a small wooden rattle and matches. The windows had been left open and the atmosphere of the room felt airy and light. There were baskets on the floor for their belongings and another small table held a basin for washing, a bar of soap and two small cotton towels.

Both Lilly and Julia were touched by the care that had gone into preparing a space for their stay. They wondered if one of the villagers had given up their home to accommodate their visitors. Both moved over to the tiny beds, sitting on the edge and gazing at each other, filled with gratitude. In time, they set about unpacking their belongings and changing into fresh and warm clothing as the temperature was dropping with the approaching evening. They rejoined Drew at the pavilion where dinner was soon to be served along with a welcoming ceremony and lively celebration in keeping with the traditions of their culture.

The next day, Drew was up and about early. He looked forward to playing the role of tour guide. A full day was soon underway. Julia and Lilly were escorted to the fields where the

Cashmere goats had first been introduced. Drew pointed out where he had set up his lean-to as the lone goatherd in the early days. The fields had been inter-planted with amaranth, quinoa and a variety of tubers for the past two years. In a few days' time, they would travel to a nearby village where the goats were being moved today. Julia and Lilly could observe the goats grazing and their capacity to clear overgrown, unproductive swaths of land that could quickly be reclaimed and transformed, soon becoming available for planting viable crops to support the community.

After the noon day meal, the three walked the narrow streets of the village. The homes were festooned with climbing vines, flowers, herbs and vegetables that provide food and medicines for the families. They occasionally saw two-story homes occupied by multi-generational families. A reciprocity existed among the villagers; on arriving into this world, one was dependent and cared for, then shown how to contribute and give back. In time, the elders would receive the assistance they needed completing the circle. There was no evidence of reticence; a natural and reciprocal cycle had been established for generations. Their nature-based spirituality provided the wisdom of interdependence. The world they inhabited informed and supported this reciprocity.

They started out at dawn the day they headed for the neighboring village where the goats were now grazing. They traveled on a familiar and well-used pack trail, burros carrying the food and water needed for the trek. Using the main road would have meant going out of their way and adding miles to their day's journey. The morning was cool starting out, but would soon give way to a pleasant warm clear day, the weather being dry and sunny in late September.

Lilly walked in the early morning light noticing the native grasses and shrubs along the path. The Peruvian feather grass was sending up slender green shoots. The *Ichu* grass, as it is commonly called, is harvested after the rainy season, cut and tied into bundles and transported by mule to where it is needed. *Ichu* has proved to be very versatile in its uses. It has been used in the construction of mud bricks and thatch for the roof of many adobe homes. Through tying techniques, bundles were formed creating the shape of a pyramid, the steep sides of the roof creating resistance to moisture. The straw is also used for insulation keeping homes cool or warm depending on the season. At times, it is used to make molds for Andean handmade cheese and is an important food for llamas, alpaca, vicuna and guanacos.

Growing among the grasses she could see vibrant green clusters, *muna*, Andean mint, a widely used Peruvian medicinal with a crisp aroma. As she gazed in the distance, she could see a patchwork of *Puya raimondii,* Queen of the Andes, towering above the surrounding vegetation. They flower every hundred years in the wild, bearing delicate white and orange flowers. Once they flower, they die.

ಬಬ

Julia walked the path at the back of the pack. Her night with Drew had rendered her silent and free of thought. In this moment, she encountered the world namelessly; she was at peace and experienced a sense of wholeness. The world at hand was strewn with exotic plants, birds and exquisite mountain views. Her curious mind would normally seek to name them, appropriate them, but not this morning. She would not shatter this precious state by bringing mind and nomenclature to it.

She saw beauty in everything; the pebbles on the road, the sound of the burros' labored breath, her mother's voice, the words she spoke no longer coagulating into meaning; she heard only the sound of her voice with its familiar cadence and inflections. All was very well with the world.

She had always been a reticent lover. When she searched deeply and honestly, she saw that she'd been afraid of being ensnared, enslaved by love. She had given herself to Drew and he to her. She had not known that lovemaking could transport you to another world by way of tenderness and acquiescence.

She had been moved. When she looked into his eyes, she'd entered a place of mystery. She gave and received, a wordless language expressed through movement and touch. She had slept peacefully afterwards, waking at times and remembering, she reached for him sustaining the connection.

She was content within her silence and reflections as they made their way to Montanita. Drew and Lilly were speaking quietly. He would occasionally look back, maintaining contact. Julia's heart swelled; a bond had been established. Where it would lead, she did not know. She did not need to know; the grace of the moment sustained her.

The path wound through hills and valleys, the terrain and vegetation changing as they slowly made their way downhill to the village. At the crest of the next hill they stopped, taking cover in the shade of the Eucalyptus growing near the path. They rested and shared food and drink. The village women had provided jars of tea for their journey; a brew of Andean mint, cilantro and black mint, a refreshing and energizing blend. Hand-sized savory pastries filled with potatoes, corn, peppers and Andean spices were passed around. These were welcomed by mid-morning after a few hours of unhurried walking. Back onto the path, they approached the next bend and Drew stopped to point out the village down below. They would arrive within the hour.

In the village they stopped briefly; Drew and his guests were greeted warmly. They then made their way to the fields where the goats were grazing. When they arrived, Lilly was surprised by the mix of colored coats. Although most of the herd was white, she saw grey, brown and a mix of black and white wide-horned goats with narrow faces.

She could see that the goats were champion foragers, that in just a few days' time most of the shrubs and vegetation had been consumed, this first field nearly cleared. How, she wondered, were they able to break down these thorny shrubs as nourishment without damaging their digestive system?

What inner chemistry and combustion were activated to support this process, she wondered.

She and Julia walked the pasture tended by the village girls who had brought the goats to Montanita. The girls would teach the goats' new caregivers how to manage the herd with the assistance of the dogs. With the onset of spring, it was also time to gather the much-prized cashmere fiber. They had brought combs to share with the new girls and began demonstrating how to hold the goats and gather the fiber.

The sun was low on the horizon when they returned to the village center where they would spend the night. Everyone gathered for an evening meal, music and singing before retiring for the night. Drew, Julia and Lilly would be heading out early in the morning, escorting the girls back to their village. Paco would be arriving within the week, setting a whole new cycle in motion.

On their return, Julia and Lilly immersed themselves in village life. Their presence was always welcomed whether they joined the girls tending the goats or helped with preparing meals. They planted trees that had been cloned from the remnants of their decimated forests. Julia joined the spinning circle in the evenings. Lilly accompanied the women who gathered plants, roots and fungi that would be used to create dyes and mordants. This information had been passed from generation to generation by word of mouth. Until recently, none of the formulas had been recorded. They relied on an intuitive process to reproduce them faithfully. Some adjustments had been made when the cashmere had been introduced. The dyes and mordants had been developed for alpaca and sheep's wool.

Lilly spent many hours among the villagers; she noted their vibrant health. They exude vitality and an ease of being. She noticed perfect white teeth, exuberant smiles and supple sun-drenched skin. They raised the food that they prepared and consumed. They labored collecting wood for heat and cooking fires, they worked the fields, harvesting and preserving the food they raised. They often walked great distances to other villages to trade and to purchase what they did not grow. These activities contributed to their fitness and stamina. The time spent in the elements contributed to their overall sense of wellbeing. They demonstrated a keen ability to surrender to the moment and to express gratitude.

She would ask permission of the village Shaman to film village life in a non-intrusive way to share her discoveries with her western students, to instill in them what was possible when balancing work and play. There was no deficit of how this was expressed in this village. She was filled with wonder as she witnessed that nearly every group activity was accompanied by song, some breaking away from their tasks to dance and add to the joy of the moment, everyone's spirits lifted by these uninhibited expressions. Some who had brought instruments would play and sing, fulfilling their role for the moment. The atmosphere was fluid and supported spontaneity and self-expression. Lilly wondered how she might convey this way of being to her duty-bound western culture; a flow, a weaving of industry and play. There was an absence of judgment and a generosity of spirit that included everyone, young and old.

Lilly rarely witnessed expressions of anger or frustration among the villagers. She wondered if perhaps her presence was affecting their behavior; she suspected not. She noticed that when faced with obstacles which did not yield to repeated efforts to correct for any given situation, they walked away, sometimes not returning to the task or situation at hand for hours or days. This was common among the adults and this way of dealing with challenges filtered down to their children and to the youngest among them. Young children were not inclined to tantrums, their frustrations short-lived. Their attention was shifted to other diversions or they received assistance in overcoming the obstacle or task at hand. Toddlers were often cared for by older children or shepherded by grandmothers. They were included in everyday activities, assimilated into village life from infancy. Infants accompanied their mothers in the fields, held while meals were prepared and while they slept.

She observed that the villagers did not rely on traditional medicine. When an imbalance occurred, they relied on natural remedies. Each family had an intimate knowledge of these common remedies. This knowledge was commonplace, as plant medicine is an integral part of traditional Andean culture. If a condition persisted, the villagers consulted the medicine women and men of the village. Healers were chosen.

Those who were called to serve the community in this way were trained by elder healers. Knowledge was passed on from one generation to the next. This required genuine spiritual knowledge and insight; power could only be acquired from the spirits. Theirs was an understanding that all persistent illness was rooted in the soul, through loss or imbalance.

She and Julia spent hours walking the acres of newly planted forest. They traveled farther to the interior where the project had begun nearly three years ago. The stand of trees and the understory were showing great vigor. Lilly at times would scoop up a handful of soil that was now a rich humus – decaying leaves, microbes, bacteria and fungi. Raising a handful to her nose, she could smell the rich tang of earth and decay. As Drew had explained, their intention was to reestablish native species, create biodiversity and restore health. Once a foothold was established, nature did the rest. The Andean oak, the *Qiwina,* as it is known in the native language of the Quechua, had been reintroduced. It is one of the hardiest trees in the world. This giant helper provides a multitude of valuable ecological functions; it prevents soil erosion, regulates the climate and provides filtration which supports natural springs. This mighty oak can also thrive on low amounts of water.

❧

Paco arrived bringing back the boys who had gone to the rainforest three months ago. He also brought a small group of boys from the rainforest who would remain here. The boys' families could not hide their excitement on seeing the group enter the village. Their friends and neighbors joined them in welcoming them home. The village came alive; much of the attention focused on the physical changes that had taken place during the boys' absence. The attention was fully turned toward them as they were greeted, teased and held.

Drew spent many hours in Paco's company for the next few days. In the evenings, Julia would join them and they would engage in lively discussions, often late into the night. The long evening conversations focused on more than the revival of ancient indigenous farming practices. Paco had been immersed in village life, and over time, he participated in community life. The lack of conflict he had come to know rested on a participatory approach to life. Communities in the rainforest were formed on a basis of cooperation and adaptation mirroring the relationships they witnessed in nature. There were disagreements to be resolved at times, but this was done with the assistance of the village elders who acted as facilitators and offered advice. In the end, those in dispute arrived at resolutions. Paco saw by contrast that the ways we interact with the world around us was what was missing in modern day culture on multiple levels.

Julia found these conversations exhilarating. One night on retiring to her room where Lilly was already fast asleep, she laid in bed reflecting. The projects that Drew and Paco had undertaken were inspiring and fueled her desire to create the village she had been envisioning for months now. In a flash, she was brought back to Sophia's parting words some months ago. Indeed, she would need to find people with expertise in many areas. What about Drew and Paco, could they be persuaded to join in? If not directly, could they become consultants as the project got underway? She would have to find the courage to discuss her intentions before she and Lilly left.

Lilly and Julia would be returning home in a matter of days. So many experiences, so much new information, new ways of seeing condensed in a few short weeks. Lilly resolved to put them into words and to fill pages with the knowledge and wisdom she'd gained. She would distill what the art of nature had revealed to her for decades now. She'd inadvertently been coaxed into seeing everything through a new prism while in Peru.

Ever since Machu Picchu, when she found herself alone, she would become preoccupied with her experience in the Room with Three Windows. Her mind would wander to quantum principles: wormholes at the Planck scale connecting us to the past AND the future. If one consciously requested information, became very still and listened, what information might be revealed? There were places, she was certain, that provided the alignment and frequency to access this information. This she believed was what had happened as she stood in front of the central window.

She had been profoundly changed by that conversation with Langston years ago. The Universe is listening, and our feedback shapes reality at all levels. Information or rather in-formation, being formed, being created, first as an idea and then into three-dimensional form. We leave trails of information as we travel through our orbit around the sun, as our galaxy spins in space. A legion of information was available to create, adapt and shape reality. She longed to share her vision, yet not entirely sure, not entirely ready.

Home Again

*O*ver time, Catherine had let go of assigning names to things; things were to be experienced. As labels disappeared, so did her preferences. There was an immediacy of experience that surfaced when naming was omitted, an observational acuity otherwise unavailable. She could not claim kindness over meanness, joy over sorrow, life over death. She had learned to claim and know Source in all things, events and circumstances. She had become a vessel willing to hold all things, to resonate with All That Is. The dropping of the body, soon now, was merely another way to acquiesce, a final yes.

She no longer required solid ground; an ice floe would do just as well. She was no longer reliant on terra firma. The formless had brought an understanding she could rest upon, free of doubt, free of preference, free of expectation. The world had become even more luminescent while Lilly and Julia had been away. She'd sequestered herself, limiting her movements to her library and her bedroom. Lilly's assistant, Molly, looked in on her every morning and every evening keeping her conversation to a minimum. She seemed to intuit Catherine's need for solitude. She brought in meals, much of them left uneaten. Catherine was retreating to another realm.

When Lilly and Julia returned, they immediately made their way to Catherine's home. They found her asleep in her study. She had a book of poems by Hafiz in her lap and a magnifying glass in her hand. She awakened suddenly, beaming as she turned her gaze to her granddaughter and great-granddaughter. She appeared physically frail to Julia who had been away for many months, but her mind was clear and her spirit came through strongly. She held out her hands to both of them; her grasp was strong and conveyed her deep affection. They sat and chatted easily as if they'd only been apart since morning.

As the dinner hour approached, Lilly left to make arrangements for food to be prepared and brought over. They spent a pleasant evening sharing the highlights of their time in Peru. As the evening light faded, Julia assisted Catherine to her bedroom and helped her prepare for bed.

Both had known what to expect on their return, yet neither was ready to say goodbye. Their first night home was a reminder that life is always in flux, nothing stays the same. Julia and Lilly took turns keeping vigil through the nights that followed. Their time with Catherine was spent in quiet celebration and in letting go. Catherine passed away on a bright fall afternoon, sitting in her library. She'd waited for a moment alone and left.

The memorial service was attended by many people spanning many generations. She had no contemporaries, having outlived them all. Still, Catherine's friendships were never defined by age. The mood was celebratory as Catherine would have wished it. The gathering was informal. Her dearest friends and family sat around recollecting and sharing private and precious moments spent in Catherine's company. She had given them the gift of being fully present, truly listening without judgement. In this generous state, she gave her guest permission to do the same. One felt more transparent and at ease in her presence, free of the encumbrance of expectation, of modifying one's communication to fit what one assumed the listener could accept or allow as possibility. What a gift it was to be truly seen, truly heard. At day's end, the guests left; Lilly and Julia sat quietly in Catherine's library, sensing her presence. They shared a glass of wine, a toast to Catherine and their fondest memories.

Lilly recalled when she'd gone to Catherine in tears, filled with despair that she would remain unable to move past the loss of Langston. Catherine had held her and once her sobs had subsided, she had told Lilly, *We all choose to come here; this worldly existence is a school. We are meant to learn and grow, we have selected circumstances and experiences that will allow us to know ourselves as an expression of the Divine. We chose to inhabit these bodies. How else could we experience the taste of salt or summer in a peach, how else to experience the meadowlark's song, to feel the summer sun on skin, to witness the undulating movement of the whisker wheat rippling across a field set in motion by a gust of wind? But our experience here bestows upon us loss, rejection, betrayal and failure, that we may know the heart in these ways too. In the stillness, in those moments when we know grace, we are neither for or against our experience. We are ambassadors and courageous volunteers on a chosen and mostly unknown path. We come to experience everything. If our hearts remain open, wide open, if we are brave and persistent, patient too, we cast light into the darkest of places.* It had been a turning point for Lilly. Her resistance had fallen away, the ache over time subsiding.

Julia recalled her visit to Catherine just before leaving for her long journey. She felt trepidation at leaving Catherine; her great-grandmother now 103, Julia feared she might not see her again. Catherine took up the role of the comforter and allayed her concerns. Catherine had told her, *there's a woman who still lives inside of me who sometimes decides she wants to go off about life's inequities. I watch and laugh at her before she gets started. Those are the good days.* Catherine had told her that our minds form ideas about how things are going to be, how we're going to feel hoping the rehearsal will shore us up for the inevitabilities. *We try to protect our hearts for what will come. It's wasted time, wasted energy,* she'd concluded, laughing. *Allow everything to unfold moment-to-moment,* she counseled. *Now, go!*

As the evening unfolded, Julia told her mother that she was in love with Drew. She shared that it had happened quite unexpectedly. How frightening it had been at first, to feel so vulnerable. She shared the plans that she, Drew and Paco had set in motion and her vision of a village.

As evening turned to night, she spoke of her time in Mexico. Julia recalled walking the streets of a tiny town in Mexico after days of ceremony in the mountains, the days preceding them spent in preparation. The dietary restrictions, the discipline and rituals were intended as purification and creating a receptive inner environment, an invitation to the spirits soon to be invoked. She was beyond tired, she teetered on exhaustion. She had journeyed to another world not without resistance and she needed time to assimilate her experience.

She walked a deserted village street. She heard music being played as she passed a home whose entrance was flanked by a profusion of chocolate cosmos and dahlias that seemed determined to thrive in spite of the dry, intense summer heat. She heard dogs barking nearby; in the distance, she heard a woman's voice singing. Julia was moved by the plaintive quality of her voice. Her steps shifted, guided by the distant voice. She walked now heading west, the voice growing clearer and louder. At last, she stood by a tiny terrace behind a small home with a west facing wall covered with morning glory whose deep purple and magenta blooms embellished the deep green vines.

The woman sat before a large empty rock vessel. She swayed as she took up a new *Ikaro*, her hands passing over the empty bowl. She suddenly opened her eyes gazing at Julia. Unaffected by the stranger's appearance she continued, her voice shifting in pitch, becoming more imploring. Julia sank

140

to the ground near the entrance to the terrace, surrendering to the fatigue and the moment. When the chant came to a close, the woman greeted Julia. She explained that she was calling in the winds and with the winds the clouds. She was praying, weaving a rain song. She had fashioned this bowl of stone many years ago, she went on to say, using another stone to create its shape over many months. Sometimes, she filled the bowl with water and offered to read the water for those who were seeking answers. Julia was intrigued. She asked Sofia if she would do a reading for her. They agreed that Julia would return in three days' time. Sofia had sensed Julia's need for rest and she wished to do a reading during a favorable phase of the moon which was nearly upon them.

Julia left and met up with friends who had participated in the Shamanic initiations. They found modest rooms and were grateful for a bed, a shower and food. The next couple days were a time of reflection and recuperation. On the day she was to meet with Sofia, Julia felt her energy returning. After dinner, she made her way to Sofia's. She had rented a moped and arrived at dusk. The terrace was softly lit up with lanterns. Sofia had brought out a rug and some cushions for the reading. She'd procured water from a nearby stream that had been left out in clay jars for the past couple nights, absorbing the energies of the sun, moon and nearby plant and animal spirits. She motioned Julia inside to shower.

Sofia had laid out a white dress and brightly colored shawl for Julia. She emerged from the tiny house and took her seat across from Sofia. Julia filled the stone vessel as Sofia instructed. Sofia had studied with The Shipibo Shamans and sang the woven songs of the Amazon. She began with *Cleansing of the Heart* and followed with *Far Away Visitors*; she then concluded with *Power Song*. Julia could hear the hush of the night as the sounds of the last *Icaro* faded away. Sofia asked Julia what medicine she wished to receive. What was to be her life's purpose, she answered. As the moon rose, illuminating the terrace and reflecting on the water's surface, the lamps were extinguished.

Sofia's hands began to move over the water; her body swayed as her hands traced complex patterns moving silently and rhythmically. Julia watched, captured by the movement; she suddenly recalled the *Vesica Piscis*, remembering it as the womb of the Universe. Her attention focused, she lost track of time. Sofia's hands came to a stop; moving fluidly, she placed them in her lap, palms facing up. She looked up and gazed at Julia. She broke the silence speaking in a softened tone.

Julia had chosen a noble path, she began. She would be called to bring about great changes, ones intimately connected with the healing of *madre Tierra*. She was not alone on this path. Many souls had chosen to incarnate at this time with a similar purpose. What her role was to be would be revealed to her in the not distant future. She would need allies to assist her in completing her mission. She would at first find the task daunting, but if she listened and remained centered, she would know what action to take. Sofia told her that the months ahead were intended for further preparation. Julia had already gathered much information which would be of great assistance in bringing her vision into form. The coming months would provide the experiences and knowledge and become a catalyst to set things in motion. Sofia suddenly fell silent. The reading was over. They moved inside; Sofia offered Julia a cool drink and they talked briefly. Julia changed and prepared to leave. Sofia followed her outside and told her to remember that limitations often foster creativity. There was an evanescent quality to these final words she'd spoken. Julia was unable to grasp their meaning; she thanked her and drove away.

Julia told Lilly that while staying at the village, she had recalled Sofia's words and she had made the decision to speak with Drew and Paco about her plans. They had listened attentively and suggested she put together a plan fleshing out her vision and its implementation. They had agreed to meet up with her at the conclusion of their projects and look at the feasibility of joining her and moving forward with the project.

Lilly felt the moment had arrived to share her experience in the Room with Three Windows. She told Julia that she had stepped into a potential future reality. She was choosing to tell her now as it related to her plans. She had seen Julia's village coming to life. Julia was with Drew and with young children. The project was ambitious and had encountered some setbacks along the way. They were moving ahead again. There were many people who were involved with the project and the foundation it rested on was collaboration. Julia had seen herself with a new partner and that they were to be among the earliest inhabitants of the village.

Lilly had a sense that time was moving as the images appeared in her vision. She saw a completed version of the village now with an active community. The originators were highly sought after as they had gained a good deal of attention over the years for their design and innovations. The village was becoming a model, a prototype for sustainable living. Groups from several places across the country and the world were coming to learn the process. They had, based on interest, created an onsite, hands-on program supported with online teaching modules as a response to the demand. The program generated income for the community for ongoing projects and further development. She and her partner served as curriculum advisors.

Lilly explained that as these visions had unfolded, they felt dream-like and had no reference point to current reality. Now that Julia had shared her vision of the village, they took on meaning. She had traveled through time covering an extensive span and yet as she surfaced when Julia had reached out to her, she'd realized that time had been compressed and that she'd traveled to a separate reality and had been gone for a matter of seconds. As Lilly's words trailed off, both realized it was nearly dawn. Julia had received yet another confirmation for her vision this evening. She felt both elation and exhaustion. They headed for home and slept knowing that Catherine had been privy to the evening's conversation. They both took comfort in this as they left her home.

ↂ

As the weeks unfolded, Julia and Lilly brought new zeal to their endeavors as they resumed their lives on the farm. Both devoted hours to writing on a daily basis; Lilly, writing her book and Julia was formulating her vision of the village she intended to bring to life. They had witnessed complex systems that served multiple functions during their time in South America and both were committed to exploring how to implement these practices on the farm and would become the premise from which the village would be developed.

One night, they both sat on Catherine's porch, where Julia was now living, making a list of the potential benefits of Cashmere goats. They would use this as a model that they would apply ruthlessly to evaluate the merits of any new introductions and existing systems. The goats cleared the land and in the process their droppings fertilized the fields. The fields, now available for food production, would provide nutrient rich soil for the production of vigorous crops for the community. Green manures grown during the fallow season would enrich the soil as would the introduction of *terra petra*. Additionally, these fertile fields would create income by selling the surplus generated. Another cascade of benefits came from the goats' fiber. The fiber harvested and turned into yarn, would then be used to produce knitted and woven goods; again, the surplus would provide additional income and give the community an opportunity to express an aesthetic unique to their region. And lastly, the goats could be loaned to neighboring communities for their benefit while providing mutual support.

The purpose of these evaluations was to create a rigorous set of conditions to be met. Namely, a list of multiple functions that served niche, biodiversity and succession. As they had observed in Peru, the key to all this was the number of connections created, not necessarily the number of functions; each element evaluated to perform as many functions as possible. Design would be planned for the immediate and the long-term returns. How many systems that were integral to creating a village would pass this litmus test? Water catchment, water treatment, drainage, shade as it relates to heating and cooling; the selection and function of trees and their impact on air quality and energy; the collection of energy and its distribution, food production, soil fertility and regeneration, home construction, recycling of water and waste management; the list went on. Each would have to be addressed. At times, the task felt daunting, but with Lilly's assistance, Julia created a format, breaking the process down into manageable classifications. There was extensive research ahead; experts would have to be sought out, often in unique niches which were introducing ground-breaking innovations and little-known disciplines. Julia knew that the months ahead would be devoted to research, meeting with experts and creating a plan based on the information gathered. In March, Drew would arrive having completed the *Meraki Project*; in mid-April Paco would follow.

ↁ

She had taken up residence in Catherine's house in the days following the memorial service. She and Lilly had gathered and donated Catherine's clothing and a good deal of her furnishings; the library remained untouched. For the time being, the house was left free of furnishings. Julia wanted to acquire what was needed in a slow organic process, making conscious choices and selecting pieces that combined both function and aesthetic. She was planning to paint the newly vacated rooms and bring a more contemporary feel to the house. Lilly supported her in her desire to make it her home. Julia was already planning for energy-efficient updates. She would use the maple that had been harvested from the sugarbush for flooring. The culling of trees was an ongoing process aimed at maintaining the health and maximizing the productivity of the sugar maples. The trees had been milled, kiln-dried and in time would be planed, sanded and used for the addition that was scheduled for construction in the spring. Julia envisioned a screened-in outdoor living room/ bedroom. Spending much of her time outdoors was essential to her well-being.

Lilly was impressed by her daughter's ambition and the breadth of the project she hoped to bring to life. After several weeks of ruminations and working with Julia on formulating a viable plan, she decided to offer a portion of the farm's two hundred and fifty acres to the development of the village. She would consult with legal counsel and find the best option for the transfer of the land and consider its covenants. She would share her intentions when she and Julia would meet next.

Endings and Beginnings

Drew was unprepared for the relationship with Julia that had so quickly unfolded over the course of just a few short weeks. Now that she had returned to the States, he missed her presence. He had not expected that they would connect so quickly and deeply. They were both disinclined to engage with anything and anyone superficially. He did not doubt her sincerity or his. Nonetheless, he was grateful for this time apart; Drew was not prone to impulsive decisions. He would allow his heart to guide him where Julia was concerned.

During the past year, he had consciously disengaged from the decision-making process of the village and the development he had initiated three years earlier. By stepping back, he was encouraging leadership among the villagers. He knew they would naturally allow intuition to guide their decisions and to trust that their age-old practices would support successful outcomes. The challenges they may face would only sharpen their abilities and build their confidence. In three-month's time, he would be leaving and he had no reservations about his departure and its timing. Through collaboration and participation, they had accomplished a great deal. He felt complete.

In the evenings, after retiring to his cabin, he frequently found himself reflecting on Julia's project. He felt a surge of excitement and admiration for her as he contemplated the scope of her project. Ideas were beginning to percolate to the surface on how to manage certain aspects of its design and implementation; land management, food production, regeneration and water management. He had started a log. He planned to share these ideas when they spoke next. Paco's input would be invaluable; his knowledge of carbon sequestering and the techniques of *terra petra* would serve them well. Lilly's innovative problem-solving skills and the willingness to go out on a limb to find solutions would provide a way to inquire into new processes and push past standard approaches. Great discoveries may be lying in wait as they embarked on this project. Drew knew that everyone's contributions would be valued and appreciated.

☙

On quiet nights, Julia would sit contemplating her plans. She felt a responsibility to communicate the nature of her mission, what lay at the heart of it. Her matrilineal ancestry informed her wisdom. She had been taught by her mother and great-grandmother that we are Spirit incarnate. We are here to learn. So much of our history up until now had been defined by survival and fear. Her intention was to assist with the birthing of a harmonious world. If our basic needs were attended to, she asked herself, our bodies nourished, our emotions expressed and released, our psyches balanced, would we not be moving toward a sense of wholeness? By integrating the needs of the heart and the needs of the soul could we not then enter a world of new possibilities? A supportive environment creates safety and freedom. No longer preoccupied with the pleas of survival, would society be at liberty to explore and expand its understanding of the nature of our journey? To question the nature of this three-dimensional reality? Time devoted to introspection, to play, to study and to inquiry could be the tinder to fuel imagination and expansion into other realms. All questions could be entertained and honored as worthy of speculation and investigation, and in time, followed by meaningful implementation.

For her, the purpose of the village was to bring more ease, more support and more freedom to its inhabitants. She did not see it as an end in itself, but rather a container that could facilitate going beyond the known in an atmosphere that supported the evolution of the human species, expanding beyond our current understanding of reality and facilitating the awakening of dormant faculties. She envisioned a kinder humanity moving toward wholeness; curious, eager to go deeper and welcoming new potentials and new information. Her vision might be seen as idyllic and naive for some. Life would never be free of so-called struggle and obstacles; challenges would always accompany growth and provide the impetus needed to discover creative solutions.

At other times, she was filled with doubts. There were areas where she had no knowledge or aptitude to bring to the table – economics for one. Creating a gifting economy with opportunities for barter and a banking system that had no precedents that she was aware of left her feeling overwhelmed. Then on reflection she realized that she could find experts that could assist her in creating a viable plan. She knew that at some point, her plan would need to address these and many other considerations. She would need to present these with a level of expertise if she hoped to find the financial backing she would need to bring her vision into reality.

Julia had recently turned her attention to assessing potential locations for the village. What geographical location would minimize the expenditure of energy? Climate was a significant factor – rainfall, availability of water. Humidity would become a factor in choosing materials suitable for home construction; it followed that raw-materials for home construction would have to be readily available from the immediate environment. The amount of sunlight and wind as potential sources of energy would greatly impact the infrastructure of the village and its dependence or independence from outside non-renewable energy sources. What states might meet these criteria and be amenable to innovative concepts, where compromises did not have to obscure the overall vision?

When she thought outside the box, she considered that the Atlanteans had developed crystal technology harnessing power for all of their energy needs. Was there anyone on the planet who had investigated the potential of or attempted to reconstruct this technology? Many Atlanteans had chosen to return to Earth at this time. Perhaps a former inhabitant would have the capacity to tap into their Akashic records and access this information? After all, for nearly a century now, many pioneers in the field of Quantum Physics held that we can instantly reclaim any information ever known. Perhaps someone had already done so? Could he or she be found?

Her studies of Vedic Architecture also informed her decision-making process; the importance of water on the land and its flow, the cardinal directions and the placement of the fire element. She had reliable resources in this area that would provide the expertise needed when the time came to decide on the overall layout of the village.

Julia's ideas about education were largely influenced by her own unconventional academics. She envisioned a hands-on approach starting at a very early age where play facilitated learning. This model honored an individual's preferences and needs, supporting and encouraging the development of one's originality and gifts. Hands were a monumental development in the evolution of our species and were connected to a portion of the brain that facilitated learning. So, a hands-on education was necessary to support the greatest level of development in early childhood.

She also was convinced that learning was a life-long process and occupation. She saw the process of teaching and learning as interchangeable and that teaching was not a profession, that everyone filled that role in their own unique capacity. She hoped to bring an informal approach to learning outside the walls of an institution, without walls or borders. In this way, curiosity would be nurtured, a natural gravitational pull prompting interest and exploration. If she erected buildings for the purpose of facilitating the learning of certain skills, they would not be known as schools. They would be multipurpose facilities that spanned a wide-spectrum of disciplines that would be available to the entire community based on interest and the desire to share important information, learn new skills, support invention and encourage creativity.

❧

On the days when she felt stymied, she would put on her hiking boots and step out into a late autumn day accompanied by Luna, once Catherine's faithful companion. In the crisp fall air, tramping fallen leaves strewn on the forest floor, she relaxed into her surroundings, recognizing her need for renewal.

In late November, she traveled to Ontario to meet with a scientist who had studied trees extensively. She had created a *bioplan*; she advocated the use of honey locusts and other trees be planted along roads to absorb pollutants. Black walnuts could be planted in areas where children play, the aerosols from the trees would stimulate their immune systems. The trees would also offer protection against UV rays. Incorporating other nut and fruit trees would provide nutrient rich foods for the community. The woodlots would provide resources for projects and additional income for community members. Julia could see that implementing *agroforestry* benefits both agriculture and the forest, from shade, to water conservation and preventing soil erosion. It supports a healthy environment, supplies food, income and beauty. Trees obviously supply multiple ecosystem services. The web of services they provide fit into the complex interconnected systems she envisioned within the village.

She returned home uplifted and ready to address other aspects of the infrastructure of the village that called for innovation; systems that turn to nature for solutions through the process of mimicry. She was ready to address sewage treatment; she made plans to travel to meet with a researcher from Oregon. She was convinced that he held the answers she was seeking. After extensive research, he had created a company that planted willow and poplar forests for the purpose of sewage treatment. Black willows proved to be especially beneficial by providing both antibiotics for insects and salicylic acid which was released into streams supporting the health of fish.

Using green infrastructure means utilizing the ecosystem of trees as natural filters with the assistance of decomposers ingesting body wastes that are transformed into materials that are cycled back as valuable soil nutrients, completing the cycle of remediation of sewage. The trees provide natural cooling system, a place to escape to replenish body and soul while being nurtured by beneficial aerosols. If only for one reason, trees should be revered for their impressive ability to sequester massive amounts of CO_2.

಄

After considerable research and consideration, Julia thought that New Mexico may be the ideal location for the village. She had spent a considerable amount of time in the high desert region of New Mexico while studying *Earthship* building methods. The weather was a big factor; the sun, the wind, the cool mornings and evenings and the availability of materials to create adobe homes. She would have Drew, Paco and Lilly weigh in on making a final determination on location. She was conflicted about discussing the location with her mom. She sensed that Lilly wanted the project to be launched here on the farm. Julia would need to present a well-thought-out plan with detailed research that supported her decision. She did not wish to disappoint Lilly and she hoped they could postpone discussing the village location until Drew and Paco arrived. She cherished her infrequent online communication with Drew and was reluctant to bring up her concerns, but she needed his input and planned to introduce the idea of location when next they spoke.

Clandestine Journey

*I*illy was taken by surprise again. She sat at a marble-top cafe table in a brick-paved alley when the realization that she'd entered that other reality suddenly struck her. She'd stepped into a tableau; the tables lining both sides of the brightly-lit alley, the vividness of the light, the brilliant blue sky. She was a stranger here in Taos, but the surroundings had suddenly taken on a surreal quality, as though a veil had been lifted and she could see, feel and observe with a degree of intensity that had not been there moments ago. She wondered if this is what Paris had been like in the latter half of the nineteenth century; an intellectual revolution and a move toward modernity that had been set in motion with the appearance of the Impressionists, a break with the past. Had they experienced this intensity and been so intoxicated by this new world that they were willing to part with convention to go deeper? Was this intoxication the foundation on which all major changes rested, she wondered?

Just days before she had watched a painter on the street in Santa Fe, his easel and canvas awkwardly positioned to capture the architectural detail of a historic building that now housed a theater, capturing with his paintbrush the light-saturated carved surfaces that would inevitably change as the hour grew. That's how she imagined Paris in the 1860s; a passionate frenzy to seize and recreate the beauty of the moment.

She'd traveled to New Mexico so she could experience first-hand why Julia was convinced that this was the ideal location for the village. Julia had been reluctant to discuss the village location; Lilly wondered why. She was eager to share her plans to deed a portion of the farm over to Julia for the project. From Lilly's perspective, this would eliminate a sizable portion of fundraising. Weeks had gone by since their return from Peru when Lilly had decided to present her idea. As soon as the conversation got underway, Julia made it clear that she would prefer to wait until Drew and Paco's arrival before tackling what she saw as an enormous decision.

Lilly was convinced that once she'd presented her offer that all other possible options would lose their appeal. As the conversation moved forward, Julia's discomfort became evident. Julia told her mother that she had suspected her intentions for weeks and she had struggled emotionally with the possibility of declining her offer. She was grateful for her mother's generosity and support, yet her intention was to create an objective atmosphere where they could entertain both the pros and cons of the farm and other potential locations. Julia felt that the presence of Drew and Paco would bring objectivity to the conversation. She invited Lilly to bring in other advisors to add to the conversation. Her intention was to choose wisely. Lilly listened, moved by her daughter's courage and circumspection.

The conversation had proceeded with more ease as Lilly realized the emotional charge it held for both of them. Lilly knew that the final decision would rest with Julia and she understood the enormity of her decision. She would welcome the input and advice of those she trusted most.

Lilly had traveled to the Willamette Valley to meet with a colleague. They were collaborating on an ambitious permaculture project that they would be presenting to a small-town council in Western Oregon in a few weeks' time. She'd decided to extend her trip by a few days with a detour to New Mexico to assess the feasibility and merits of locating the village in the high desert of the Southwest. She had contacted a realty company to inquire about the availability of land that could meet their essential criteria. The realtor had two locations he thought might be of interest to her.

Lilly was ambivalent about sharing the reasons for her delayed return with Julia. She needed this experience to free herself of bias. This area of the country was unfamiliar to her. As she sat at the cafe table, deep in thought, she understood why this region was known as the land of enchantment.

Lilly traveled southeast from Taos to meet with the realtor the next morning. The first property she viewed would support the project in terms of size but offered little in terms of aesthetics, a reliable water source or the essential features that were needed to make the project financially feasible.

The following morning, they met at a lovely location set in a valley, among mature trees, tall grasses, hills and a stream that benefited from the winter run-off from the mountains in the distance. Lilly had been taken aback by the beauty of the place. Swales would obviously be needed in a climate with an annual rainfall below twenty inches. So would building humus which did not appear to be plentiful here. This climate would require multi-layered water strategies, soil building, dense plantings; packing and stacking to create shade. Shading soil could effectively impact water loss. Mulching would also assist in conserving water and in time, microclimates could be identified and their features put to maximum use. She left with food for thought.

On the flight home, Lilly spent some time reflecting on the events of the past few days. Her visit had spawned many questions and new considerations. Should Julia decide on the farm as the village site, the permaculture program and the test plots would prove invaluable to the development of the village. The village would provide internship opportunities for students across multiple disciplines, be it alternative home building, water conservation and catchment, alternative energy sources and consumption. By collaborating with the school, the village would greatly reduce their costs, benefiting from learning valuable skills in exchange for labor. Much of the information needed in little known areas could become research projects pursued by interested students. Once completed, the merits of potential systems would be evaluated prior to implementation. Lilly was considering establishing a western campus in the event New Mexico was selected for the village site. She made notes of these ideas that she could later present when they were ready to entertain the site location.

Growing Vision

With fewer distractions while Lilly was away, Julia had turned her attention to fleshing out other aspects of the project. She had imagined a limited number of vehicles in the village, and would propose shared ownership of vehicles. An area at the entrance to the village would be designated for parking, thus eliminating the need for paved streets and the cost of their maintenance, as well as garages attached to homes. Eliminating these features would improve the aesthetic of the village. Battery-powered and hand-pulled carts would be available in an adjacent area to transport goods from vehicles to homes over short or long distances. Julia was always looking for ways to reduce and eliminate dependence on fossil fuels. Leaving vehicles at the entrance would greatly affect the overall air quality within the village.

Construction of homes would begin from the interior of the site, new homes added on the perimeter facilitating new construction and easy access for necessary equipment. Home placement would be determined based on the natural features of the land and the suitability of a home within that environment. Homes would be designed with a small footprint. Some home designs would feature a shared central living area with wings for the residents to retreat to including a sitting room, bedroom, private bath and outdoor space. Joint ownership would reduce the cost of building, encouraging community living and mutual social support.

Julia understood that what she planned was experimental and subject to review, knowing adjustments would likely be needed along the way. The surrounding environment would dictate the features of the village with homes placed within the natural environment rather than nature surrounding homes. Natural habitats would be maintained for recreation and for the purpose of study. Public spaces would feature the art of nature: stone fountains, bronze and concrete sculptures depicting nature in its rich diversity, adding to the serenity of these spaces.

A Village Within a Forest concept would also provide some unique economic opportunities such as forest therapy inspired by the forest bathing practice of Japan. A learning center and additional housing could eventually be added to accommodate visitors and those eager to learn about the benefits of this new living concept. Extended stays could be arranged for those wishing to explore joining the community.

She had created a list of community projects; she'd planned for a labyrinth, perhaps two, at strategic locations. Teams of community members would spearhead the development and maintenance of shared communal spaces and recreational areas. She envisioned a community center where meetings and trainings could be held and become a space for social gatherings. With a multi-purpose design, they could facilitate educational events and possibly include sleeping rooms for guests who were visiting family and friends of the community. After the holidays, she planned to research and create a preliminary model of the economic system for the community. She had met James, an ecological economist from Vancouver, on her return flight from Ontario in October. They had struck up a conversation and exchanged information. She'd been in touch and set up an initial session to discuss her ideas in early January.

❦

Within days of her return from New Mexico, Lilly and Julia traveled to Colorado to purchase a small herd of Cashmere goats. Lilly had been greatly inspired by the goat project while in Peru. Drew had built in layers of redundancy with the introduction of the goats when he first launched the *Meraki Project*. Function stacking has cumulative effects and had led to great success and multiple sources of income for the villagers.

She had worked diligently for weeks since her return from Peru putting together a program that she had subsequently presented to a private school with an agriculture-based program. She had proposed the introduction of Cashmere goats to their program. She and Julia had devised a curriculum and would be supervising the program closely. After an introductory meeting and several presentations outlining the purpose and merits of the program, the Board of Directors had agreed.

Lilly and Julia had presented video footage from the *Meraki Project* pointing out the unique traits of the Cashmere goat, their ability to consume noxious weeds, thereby eliminating the use of chemical pesticides and herbicides. Lilly had sold them on the idea that by expanding their programs, they would inevitably increase their enrollment. Diverse disciplines resulted in greater appeal to greater numbers. Under this umbrella, they would also be introducing a textile program to utilize the harvested cashmere fiber. They would be working in collaboration with the local Spinning and Weaving Guild and the County Art Center.

The goats would arrive within weeks after their return from Colorado and would initiate a flurry of activity for both Lilly and Julia. As the goats were acclimating to their new environment and the school's able staff put them to work observing their activity and making fields notes for future reference, they would both need to be on hand to field any questions and assist with the process of launching a new program.

November was here and the activity on the farm was winding down in step with nature's approaching dormant cycle. Julia and Lilly were both more focused on research, cooking and time indoors as Thanksgiving approached. It was a time to go within and replenish the energy expended in the past few months and appreciate where life was guiding them as each day unfolded.

Drew would be coming in December. He had planned a visit to his parents some time ago and would now extend his stay to be with Julia. Both were finding it challenging to be apart; their FaceTime sessions made it obvious to both of them. Drew invited Julia to join him at his parents' home in Virginia for a few days. They would drive back to the farm together in time for a winter solstice ceremony.

Every year since Julia and Lilly could remember, they had held a Solstice Ceremony. Catherine had started the tradition when Lilly was still a girl. At first, there were just a handful of participants; but over the years as more people were shifting their focus to nature-based honoring, the numbers attending had grown. More than forty years ago, Catherine had created a labyrinth where the ceremony was held. The labyrinth would be alight with luminaries on the shortest day of the year in the northern hemisphere. The initial ceremony would be followed with the burning of the wreaths that had been created from holly, barberry and fir trimmings in November. Now dry, they would be set on fire and rolled up the hill bursting into flame signifying the return of the sun as they rolled back down. Catherine had borrowed this tradition from the ancient Celts who had performed a similar ceremony centuries before. It was believed that these burning wreaths representing the sun had inspired the origin of the Christmas wreath. The fireplace in the barn would be lit in the hours prior to the ceremony to warm the space and a feast would follow. Warm stews, fruit cobblers and mulled wine would be served to the guests in attendance and the evening would conclude with improvisational music provided by some of their guests.

Reunion

*J*ulia could barely contain her excitement the day she left
for Virginia. The weather looked promising without any
snow in the forecast. She left early in the morning and would
arrive late in the afternoon. Lilly saw her off, sharing in the
excitement of her daughter's reunion with Drew.

As she pulled into the serpentine tree-lined drive, she
could see lights from the house between the trees as dusk was
approaching. As she made the last turn, she saw Drew on the
front porch of his parents' renovated colonial home waving to
her. They both had longed for this moment. Demonstrating
the joy of their reunion would have to wait until later. Drew
greeted her at the car, embraced and kissed her warmly.
They made their way to the front door hardly aware of their
surroundings.

Drew led the way to the kitchen where Marcy and Jack
were busy with dinner preparations. They greeted Julia with a
warm welcome. Jack and Drew made their way out to gather
Julia's things and move her car to a sheltered area. On their
return, Jack opened a bottle of wine and offered a toast to
welcome Julia and to the evening ahead; Drew offered to set

the dinner table and Julia joined in. It was the perfect excuse to spend a few moments alone together.

The dining and living area had a large stone fireplace and a wall of windows; outside, shrubs, ornamental trees and a bird-feeding area provided a backdrop, a natural canvas. The ceilings featured dark original beams, the walls were painted white giving the room a crisp and bright look. A window seat ran the length of the wall of windows covered with comfy and colorful cushions and throws, this area designed to take in the outdoor scenery and wildlife activity.

Marcy was a potter and had created the dinnerware. The beauty of it and its informal natural attributes were not lost on Julia. A large hand-built pottery bowl sat in the center of table was filled with pine cones, black walnuts, now-dry catalpa seed pods and recently added yew and spruce clippings. The arrangement was stunning. Three brass candlesticks of varying heights flanked each side of the centerpiece, holding candles of burnt orange.

Marcy and Jack soon joined them; they sat in the living room warmed by the fire while dinner roasted in the oven. The conversation turned to Drew's project and its nearing completion. Had he not been returning to Julia and another ambitious project it might have been more difficult for Drew to leave Peru and the thriving village community he had become a part of. Over dinner, the conversation shifted to Julia. Marcy and Jack wanted to know what had inspired her vision for a village community. Had she launched into this conversation, she explained, they could conceivably be at the dinner table until dawn. She begged off and promised that in the next couple days, she would provide them with the background that had given birth to the idea.

The conversation shifted and the evening proceeded with delightful stories about Drew's childhood along with some laughter at Drew's expense. By the evening's end, Julia was moved by how much Drew's visit meant to his parents. She decided to extend an invitation for them to join her family and friends for the solstice celebration at her home. They could have more time with Drew and she knew that Lilly would gladly welcome them. Both Marcy and Jack were touched by her invitation but at first declined. Julia insisted that they give it more consideration. With Jack acquiescing that he and Marcy would discuss her generous offer, the evening came to a close. Marcy and Jack retired to the kitchen to tidy up and Drew and Julia stepped out with the family dogs into the crisp December night. The dogs headed for the nearby fenced meadow and they followed. The dogs were not deterred by the cold night air and the light dusting of snow. They romped and circled back approaching Drew affectionately with tails wagging, enjoying their long-awaited reunion.

When they returned to the house, the lights had been dimmed and Jack and Marcy had gone to bed. Drew found a warm blanket and invited Julia to sit with him by the fireplace. Both seemed at a loss for words. Eight weeks had gone by since Julia and Lilly's departure, yet both sensed that the time apart had not diminished their feelings. Both knew that the desire to express their love in the ways only new lovers can, was not going to happen that night. Julia could not conceive of sharing a bed with Drew in his parents' home. That reunion would have to wait until they were at Julia's home at the farm. She wanted their physical intimacy to feel unencumbered, free to surrender without reservation. They talked quietly late into the night; Hours later, Drew walked her to the guest room.

The next day, after an elaborate breakfast, they dressed warmly, ready to explore the farmstead. Jack escorted them to his well-equipped woodworking room attached to the garage. They then fed the chickens and guinea hens who seemed quite comfortable on their perches warmed by the heat lamps that hung from the low-pitched ceiling of the chicken coop. They walked the orchard and made their way to Marcy's studio. There were kilns that lined the wall of the room and shelves and shelves of pieces ready to fire. In the glazing room, Julia saw a collection of what must have been prototypes. They'd gathered clay dust and had apparently been shelved there for a while: vases, bowls, pitchers, some in salt-glaze finishes, some pit-fired and stone polished, others in matte glazes in muted colors, displayed for inspiration; a catalog of Marcy's creations.

They left the studio and made their way over to the horse barn. The barn held several stalls although most of them were unoccupied; Marcy and Jack kept only a couple of mares now. The temperatures were rising and the sun was out. Julia and Drew would ride this afternoon. There were light-dappled wooded trails and open pastures that bordered the neighboring property that would make for a perfect early winter ride.

☙

Drew and Julia left early on Wednesday three days before the solstice. Marcy and Jack would follow the next day. They would have a day to share with Lilly before the celebration and they had volunteered to help with the festivities as needed. Both were accomplished cooks and could help with food preparations and assist with readying the barn for guests, transforming it into a magical place.

The drive back to the farm was uneventful. Marcy had helped Julia pack a luxurious lunch which would easily outshine any restaurant options they may have considered on the drive back. The day-long drive seemed to go by quickly, Julia and Drew exchanging playful banter and listening to music. The miles passed by and they arrived at the farm just before dusk, greeted by Lilly and an entourage of farm dogs rushing out of the house to greet them.

In the days following the solstice celebration, Julia and Drew spent many hours discussing the many aspects of creating a new community based on principles of cooperation. Julia asked for Drew's input on community conflict resolution. She hoped that Drew's experience with the *Quechua* community would shed some light on an effective process. She was concerned about the strong independent spirit that had and still pervaded American culture and how it would play out in working toward consensus. The two cultures were worlds apart; one feminine and founded on cooperation, the other masculine and adamant about personal freedoms. This aspect of creating community seemed pivotal to its success and would require a shift from *me* to *us* from all members. What process and dialogue might they implement that would generate mutual respect and assist the members in entertaining different points of view?

Drew shared the *Quechuas'* methods in detail, yet both felt that a new process would need to evolve for this community if it were to bring about positive outcomes. Drew suggested reaching out to existing intentional communities to get their input. With a history in place, they may have valuable information to share which might help them avoid the pitfalls that they had identified and had adjusted for.

Drew had spent time drawing sketches of possible home sites. The landscaping surrounding them included fruit & nut trees, mixed with native deciduous hardwoods; below these there was an understory of shrubs, flowers and edibles that would benefit from the cool and the shade. Herbs and greens were located close to the house. The surrounding gardens had been planned with swales and other water catchment features that would reduce the use of additional water sources. Beds within the permanent garden spaces could easily become tunnel houses to extend the growing season and protect seedlings in the spring. The system created a habitat for wildlife, insects and microorganisms. The design resulted in a cooling environment in the growing season and a buffer from wind and cold during the fall and winter which would reduce the energy needs of the homes. The plants and layout were hypothetical and would remain this way until a location had been determined.

Drew also shared some important considerations in choosing a location. They would need to research and consider zoning policies and the overall acceptance of the larger community to welcoming a community with innovative concepts whose values were considerably different. Philosophical differences with regards to alternative construction and energy and a self-sufficient economy could trigger resistance on multiple levels from different factions, Drew thought. They were undertaking a noble endeavor and implementing much needed changes, but he cautioned Julia to be prepared for resistance and obstacles along the way. The project would be better received in a progressive community. In all likelihood, the village would have to evolve in stages to allow for acceptance and provide education of their more innovative ideas. Julia was initially perplexed by these new considerations, but she trusted Drew's judgment and knew that he brought a level of realism that tempered her ideals.

On Drew's last day, Julia expressed her ambivalence about her mother's offer to use the farm for her village. Drew listened attentively and cautioned her not to eliminate the farm as a possibility, but rather to allow the process of in-depth research to provide the pros and cons of any one location. She was touched by his unbiased perspective.

That evening Julia, Drew and Lilly spent the evening reminiscing about their time together in Peru, discussing the newly-launched Cashmere goat program he had inspired, and Catherine's passing. They had walked to the oak grove that afternoon where her ashes had been spread. Lilly & Julia had commissioned a bronze sculpture of a young woman dancing with birds perching on her arms as she moved. It would be placed in the grove in the spring in Catherine's memory and as a tribute to her life.

Parting was bittersweet for both Drew and Julia. In a few weeks they would begin their life together in earnest. They both had plenty to occupy their time in the meantime, but they had gotten a taste of what it would be like to live side-by-side. They drove to the airport mostly silent, just holding hands.

☙

The months that followed moved by quickly. Julia spent hours researching LLCs, zoning laws in several locations, getting familiar with the legal requirements of creating an intentional community, which she discovered was financially identical to creating a condominium association. None of these seemed to resonate. Her research led her to Community Land Trusts. She needed an option that would release them from operating within a system she was looking to leave behind. For Julia, explicit common values included a new means of governance and was the foundation on which the community would be created, counter-cultural in nature. She envisioned a home ownership collective with the active participation of the residents in the planning of the community.

Community Land Trusts were created to hold lands in perpetual trust for the permanent use of rural and urban communities. She discovered that the first CLT had been started by a group affiliated with the Civil Rights movement and located in Georgia; it gave a community of African Americans access to rural lands. Community Land Trusts were based on the Indian *Gramdan*, a village gift movement, and the *moshav* community lands that were owned by the Jewish National Fund. She was greatly encouraged; this could be a working model.

In February, she and Lilly would attend a workshop on the legal basics for intentional communities, an important consideration that would inform decision-making and strategic planning going forward. As Drew had suggested, she had identified organizations that offered training in community organizing, planning, project management and team leadership.

❧

Lilly traveled to Western Oregon for her presentation in favor of an ecologically-based innovative system as the town of Mavis prepared to upgrade or remediate their water treatment system. She and her colleagues had spent the past months creating an alternative to a traditional sewage system that expended massive amounts of energy and resulted in higher utility charges for the townspeople. She presented a system that was based on a man-made marsh, aquatic plants, a variety of organisms and bacteria that would break down waste. This system would cost more to implement initially, but reduce the town's operational costs significantly over the course of the coming years.

Beyond the water system, she presented additional plans for reducing the town's overall energy costs. In her model, the city would provide and plant shade trees for homeowners; planted near the house, the trees would reduce both heating and cooling costs. She presented drawings of clustered plantings near municipal buildings, choosing from a variety of species and size to add beauty to function. Their plan included the creation of a forest above the town that would funnel air into the city center and provide a recreational area for the community. Designed with trails and benches, the trees would be tagged identifying the various species. This woodland would also serve as a wildlife habitat and a nature education sanctuary.

ᢙᢒ

Julia woke up one morning feeling anxious and unsettled. She had been feeling a growing sense of urgency and the overwhelm of taking on a great responsibility as she delved deeper into her mission. She got up and moved into her morning rituals starting with inspirational readings and meditation.

In the silence she followed a thread that led her to the source of her unrest. She realized that her attention had shifted to managing the emergence of her brainchild from her intellectual perspective. She knew that intuition had been pushed aside, at times dismissed, now guided mostly by her wants. In order to meet her expectations, she was *pushing the river* at the cost of her inner wellbeing. She began tearing up realizing she'd provoked the state she was in with her own relentless pursuit of questions that could not immediately yield answers.

She now found herself breathing more deeply, releasing the tension she'd held onto the past couple weeks. The wiser part of her knew that answers offered themselves unbidden once demands and urgency subside. She decided to get dressed and go for a walk. It was a cold winter day but the sun was shining this morning. She would take the dogs with her. She would give herself a day of leisure with no agenda, let her inner promptings guide her, allowing her intuition and higher-self to guide and bring her to a centered place.

Luna and Star greeted her at the barn. The fresh air and sunshine brightened her spirits. At first, she walked aimlessly, her heart and mind focused on her surroundings. Catherine came to mind and she found herself moving in the direction of the oak grove. She made her way to the meadow where Catherine's ashes had been scattered. She relaxed on entering this private sanctuary. Breathing more deeply now, she moved through the tangle of dissonance of the past few days and found a way to quiet her mind and listen to her heart. She felt Catherine's presence, and her burden lessened.

What had Catherine taught her by example? She knew that her warrior spirit was not serving her. She need not do battle with a nameless imaginary enemy. She need not create resistance to what existed only in her mind, what she now perceived as insurmountable obstacles. She realized the expenditure of energy she was wasting on a battlefield of her own creation. Her imagination had run rampant feeding the wrong wolf.

She suddenly laughed and cried at the same time. Her yearning and deep sense of responsibility had run wild. The image of an unbridled stallion came to mind. She would need to guard against this tendency. Catherine would have insisted on the merits of these attributes when carried in a balanced manner, the task of the warrior, the task of all beings. In her efforts to serve Gaia she had forgotten to connect to her Source, she had forgotten to call upon her allies to guide her. She would stop for a while and listen, call on *Woman Medicine* and allow the process to become more playful and for things to unfold with right timing.

Leaving the oak grove feeling lighter than she had for days, she was reminded of nature as medicine; *friluftsliv* came to mind, a Nowegian lifestyle approach. Living outdoors is deeply ingrained in Norwegian culture; they possess a great affinity for celebrating time spent outdoors in any weather conditions. She recalled that *friluftsliv* had been inspired by the playwright Henrik Ibsen.

She slowly made her way to the school's well-stocked kitchen and collected what she needed to prepare dinner. She was inspired to cook. She reached out to her mother and the Solarzano elders and invited them to dinner. She then casually made her way home pulling a cart filled with the items for her carefully thought-out dinner.

Settling back into her home, she warmed herself with a cup of tea, a blend of lemon verbena, mint and lavender grown and blended here on the farm, a brew inspired by Buddhist monks. She turned on some music and made her way to her desk inspired to write poetry.

By midafternoon she turned her attention to dinner. She would serve a winter squash and cider soup seasoned with thyme and garnished with caramelized onions; she would roast a spatchcocked chicken with lemons under the skin served with oven-roasted root vegetables. She would prepare a simple arugula salad with sliced fresh pears and *Cambozala* cheese tossed with a Dijon-maple vinaigrette. She would uncork a bold red wine she had brought back from Peru. After the meal, they would retire to the living room warmed by the wood burning stove and follow dinner with apple crisp served with crème anglaise and whipped cream.

The Solarzanos left after an evening of warm and animated conversation. Lilly helped Julia clean up before heading home.

Heading down the hall on her way out, she'd been drawn to Julia's lit study. On the computer screen she read:

In culvert homes
with grooms of doom,
I pass the night.
Away from the towering madness,
the bliss of small.

Eccentricities ravish the tenants
Still, quiet in their own way.
Patently forgotten and wishing it so;
the braille and seeing dogs of the underground,
the root canal along which all baseness passes.
Things discarded, perused for value.

She was touched by Julia's writing. She found herself scrolling down curious to know if there were others to be found.

One Plus One Equals

An accumulation of thought, friction, feelings
Minus
A disavowal of life
Plus
The murmur of a brook
Reduced by
The incessant clicking of the keyboard,

the hum of the hard drive
Minus
The ceaseless drive toward ease
Equals...

Squared by a kiss
Reduced by jealousy
Divided by envy

Multiplied a hundred-fold by
Faith
Trust
Reduced almost completely by hatred
Carried to infinite places by Love

Lilly suddenly became aware that her curiosity and appreciation of Julia's poetry was an invasion of her daughter's privacy. She quickly left the room knowing that if Julia deemed that these new poems had any merit, she would gladly share them.

Julia spent the next couple days reconnecting with simpler rhythms guided by her inner compass. She devoted many hours to writing poetry, walking and immersing herself in the winter landscape. She remembered what it felt like just being. She emerged from this retreat with a fresh perspective. Perhaps her initial project could evolve on a smaller scale. The land here on the farm offered a unique opportunity of bypassing legalities and protracted meetings and building permits. Tiny houses now began to have an appeal as did small structures that fell outside the parameters of permit requirements. This could be a first effort to inform future and more ambitious projects.

She saw a willingness among young people to do with less and to experiment; they were ready to embrace a new paradigm. For older generations it would mean releasing the old story, a story deeply embedded in a multi-generational web. She understood that it could be frightening to release the known when everything around you is telling you it is time to let go. Stepping into the unknown often unleashes fear unless one has a highly-developed sense of adventure and a well-developed sense of faith and trust.

After a few days of ease and relaxation, she felt ready to approach the project from a fresh perspective. She had a Zoom session scheduled that afternoon with James, the green economist she had met in the fall. Her agenda was implementing ecocentrism and finding alternatives to capitalism. They spoke for nearly two hours. They discussed community-based economics, practicing voluntary simplicity, local purchasing, a gifting economy, shared resources and a time-share bank.

They spoke about living simply, reducing one's possessions, the rise of *cottagecore,* a return to increased self-sufficiency and the work and live balance. They discussed the principles of Deep Ecology, the inherent values of *Open-Air Philosophy* and a holistic vision of the world with humans as part of the ecosystem. Their conversation boosted her confidence and she was fortified by the knowledge that many of these alternatives to a capitalist economy were being implemented by small communities in parts of Europe and other parts of the world.

James encouraged her to broaden her vision, to add to the details of a time-share bank before their next meeting. He thought that this would be a great way to reduce the need to exchange money. By reducing income, the community would inadvertently reduce their tax obligations. It effectively added another layer of self-sufficiency, and would encourage interdependence in the community. As the session came to a close, she felt that she had found an ally; besides, he was a fan of Vedic architecture and Earthships.

During their next session, they addressed the benefits of community solar versus single-home energy expenditures. They spoke at length on the virtues of a local currency, another principle of New Economics. James shared a list of well-known organizations and offered a reading list that would assist her in developing her vision in this area.

Marshall Stewart

*L*illy met Marshall following the Mavis town meeting. He had walked up to congratulate her on her fine presentation. He had traveled from Washington state having taken a great interest in the water treatment debate in the town of Mavis. He had read an article in an environmental publication a few months ago that had brought Lilly's proposal to his attention. Eastern Oregon has a more conservative way of life. Mavis had elected Jack Lathrop as Mayor during the last local election, a young forward-thinking politician. He had studied environmental science and was a great advocate of Deep Ecology. If the town council voted in favor of the ecologically-based wastewater treatment, this would put their town on the map, bringing attention to a small community who dared to think big.

Marshall thought that the energy saving plan she had tagged on was a great way to help guide the town toward sustainable solutions for future infrastructural development. He called it *sowing seeds*. He was warm and genuine. He knew Jack Lathrop, Lilly learned, and had consulted with Jack on several occasions following his election to discuss the future of the town. They had met serving as board members of a prestigious environmental organization on the East Coast the previous year.

Marshall had studied ecology and gone on to research and design regenerative permaculture methods. He had started out with home-scale designs in the Seattle area and as his passion evolved, his interest had shifted to larger scale models for towns and small cities. Lilly appreciated his ambition and enthusiasm. Master a skill on a small scale, she thought, and then allow your vision to grow. *We have entered a time when all of us need to take our skills into the wider world*, she shared.

Lilly talked about her daughter's ambitious project and asked if she could get his contact information. She knew Julia would appreciate his knowledge and experience. Lilly noticed that the council members were patiently waiting and were eager to comment on her presentation. Jack walked up and shook Marshall's hand and Lilly turned her attention to the town council members.

An hour later she left the hall with the mayor, who walked her to her hotel just a couple blocks away. Jack was optimistic and told her he'd be in touch as soon as the council met again. She told him that she would be available to answer any questions or concerns he or the members may have before or during the meeting.

The hotel lobby was quiet on a weeknight. She made her way to the newly-renovated bar and took a seat at one of the high-top tables lining the wall of windows. She ordered

a Pinot Noir from Oregon, her way of saying *job well done!*
As the server returned with her wine, she spotted Marshall
entering the hotel lobby. Apparently, he was a hotel guest. He
turned toward the bar and saw her and she asked if he would
like to join her.

They easily fell into conversation; they shared many
interests and she was enjoying his company immensely. He
suddenly seemed so familiar and then there it was; he was the
man in her vision at Machu Picchu! She had stopped talking
mid-sentence and Marshall looked at her curiously. Somewhat
befuddled, she waved away his concern and resumed the
conversation. As the conversation turned to projects and
interests, Langston's name popped up. Marshall was familiar
with Langston's work and had met him many years ago at a
conference. Some years later, in search of information that
Langston had authored, he had learned of his death. Nearly
thirty years later, Lilly was able to pay tribute to her late
husband without tears. She gave Marshall a sense of the brief
and beautiful life they had shared together. The conversation
had reached a turning point; both noticed the time. They
sensed the evening was at an end. Following an exchange of
good nights, they each made their way to their rooms.

Lilly found herself smiling as she washed her face and
prepared for bed. She rather liked Marshall Stewart. Her
breath caught recalling the vision from the Room with
Three Windows. She suspected that their paths would cross
again. She knew that Julia would be eager to hear how the

presentation had gone, but she fell into bed and immediately fell asleep. The call would wait until tomorrow.

❧

She had a midmorning flight but would have to drive a distance to the airport. The alarm startled her out of sleep before it was light out. Within an hour she had dressed, ordered coffee and packed the rental car. She had yet to reach out to Julia, but she needed to be on her way. She settled into the drive and reflected on her presentation and her time with Marshall. She was deep in thought as she approached the airport exit when her phone rang. It was Julia; she wanted to know who Marshall Stewart was. Lilly was surprised; he had wasted no time reaching out to her daughter. Julia went on to explain that an email had arrived a few minutes ago from Marshall Stewart from a company called *Earth Wonder*. He'd mentioned meeting Lilly in Mavis. He had mentioned the village project and offered his services should she be interested. Julia had yet to look at his website. Her curiosity got the better of her and since she'd not heard from Lilly, she'd decided to call.

Lilly smiled listening to her daughter's words. She explained the circumstances of meeting Marshall and gave her some of the highlights of his work. She added that he might be a great resource for Julia and that she had shared her information with him. There was a long pause on the other end and then Julia said, *I feel that there is more to this story than you are letting on.* Lilly laughed and let her daughter know that she had arrived at the airport and would need to continue this conversation at a later time.

The call ended and Julia immediately turned her attention to researching *Earth Wonder*. She discovered that Marshall Stewart was an attractive and intelligent man. His work in the last decade had focused on a synergy of micro and macro permaculture designs within communities. Doing a new search, she found his name in an Ag-Environmental publication that did an extensive article featuring his work and accomplishments. A search for permaculture in Seattle yielded several newspaper articles and many photos of his earlier work. Still, she felt there was something of a more personal nature about this man appearing at this time; he was the same age as Lilly.

Lilly sat at the airport waiting to board her connecting flight when her phone rang. She picked up without checking her caller ID, certain it was Julia. She heard a man's voice; it was Marshall. He was driving home to Washington and wondered how her travel day was going? Lilly laughed, surprised to hear from him. There was such an ease and frankness to his communication. He mentioned that he had reached out to Julia before leaving Mavis, and when could they meet up again? Julia was both speechless and charmed. She had not traveled this road in some time. He would be speaking at a Midwestern Permaculture Conference in March, perhaps she could meet him there or he could drive out to the farm after the conference? She asked him to forward the conference information. March was a busy month -spring planting, sugaring season – so perhaps visiting the farm might be a better alternative, she offered. He seemed delighted with the prospect of visiting the farm, experiencing the hands-on program she had developed and meeting Julia.

And so, their story began, unexpectedly and with ease. Julia's jaw would drop when she learned that the man in her vision was Marshall Stewart. She would be waiting at baggage claim when Lilly landed and no doubt eager for a long chat on the drive home.

There were only a few short weeks before March arrived and Lilly marveled at how easily her life had shifted to include Marshall. They were in constant communication: phone, email and Skype. There was an ease and sweetness that permeated their time together, no matter what form it took. The pleasantness of this newfound connection elevated her every action whether making up her bed, having a cup of tea or taking out the trash. She did not question or need to know where this was headed; in her heart she knew.

Julia had been full of questions on the ride home. She stared aghast when Lilly told her who he was, the man in her vision. She could barely contain her excitement! For some time now, she had wished that her mother would find love again, and here he was as big as life, an unexpected surprise.

Julia started her own communication with Marshall. She found him to be affable and generous with his time. Soon after their first communication, he forwarded articles he had written.

They were filled with valuable knowledge that addressed issues she had not considered at this stage. She was grateful; better forearmed, she thought, shorten the learning curve from the experience of those who had already traveled this road.

His reading list arrived and he encouraged her to do some research on E. F. Schumacher, a forward-thinking economist, known for his human-scale approach. *Local Resources for Local Needs,* was a tag phrase of his. He was a proponent of self-reliant economics. Schumacher mentioned that he had been influenced by Gandhi's concept of *Economy of Permanence.* Marshall recommended she read the paper Schumacher had authored that had brought him to prominence, *Multi-Lateral Clearing,* and to get a copy of the book he had written in the early seventies, *Small is Beautiful: A Study of Economics: As If People Mattered.* Marshall was certain that Julia would find him to be a kindred spirit.

Indeed, he was; he favored appropriate technology whose criteria was defined by the scale of the community. This was an individualized approach, an economy of place, taking unique traits and variables into consideration; not a cookie-cutter approach. Julia read that he had started out in life as an atheist; once he had abandoned materialism, he became interested in religion. He studied Buddhism; this led to his development of a set of principles he called *Buddhist Economics* that focused on the primacy of human development.

He believed that Gandhi was the *people's economist* and that his economic views were aligned with spirituality rather than materialism. How fortuitous that Marshall had brought E F Schumacher's work to her attention. She felt fortified and no longer a pioneer without forebears. How had this man's work escaped her attention all this time? She left her desk and headed for Catherine's library. She searched the rows of shelves, and, as she suspected, found a copy of *Small Is Beautiful* and his later publication of *A Guide for the Perplexed.* Had she thought to search the library when she first learned of Schumacher, she could have saved herself the cost of and the time she waited for the book to arrive. Catherine's copy was a 1975 edition. She couldn't wait to share her latest discoveries with Drew. She shot off a brief email requesting a FaceTime session in the next few days. Chances were, he was aware of Schumacher's work and they had not yet had a chance to discuss him in terms of the project. Her excitement grew as she realized that these were the principles on which her vision rested: spirituality and economy, spirituality and ecology, spirituality and the evolution of mankind.

Her confidence grew in her ability to create a workable plan. With the aid of so many capable people within her reach, she knew her chances for a successful outcome were more than likely. Just as the saying *It takes a village to raise a child* implies, Julia understood that it also takes many hands, many voices to create a village. And the help seemed to arrive from many sources in unpredictable ways fueled by generosity. These were gifts for which she felt immeasurable gratitude.

ↅↄ

The weeks had flown by. Lilly had decided to fly to Wisconsin for Marshall's presentation and they had agreed to rent a car and drive back to the farm once the conference ended. Lilly had gone to some lengths to prepare for his visit. She'd cleaned the guest room on the second floor, freshening all the bedding. She'd brought in a desk that would allow him to work remotely as needed. She planned for more elaborate meals and looked forward to a visit to the Farm School so Marshall could experience the new program with the Cashmere goats. The timing was perfect as the students would be harvesting the Cashmere undercoat as spring arrived. Drew would be arriving at that time and had volunteered to demonstrate the process. He was bringing tats, the combs from the Himalayas used for this purpose.

Depending on the spring temperatures, they might still be collecting sap at the farm and finishing maple syrup production. This was a task that Lilly got behind. For her, it represented the start of the new spring work cycle. A new group of students would be arriving at the farm as spring marked the beginning of the calendar year for the permaculture program. The second-year students would assume the responsibility of initiating the newcomers and introducing them to the multiple disciplines.

ᐁ

Lilly sat in the audience listening to Marshall's presentation. He seemed so at ease; engaging too. In this regard, he reminded her of Langston. For both these men, it seemed as though monumental problems could readily be broken down into surmountable tasks regardless of how dire the reality of the situation appeared to others. Both had the largesse of spirit to hold to the possibility that a new course could be adopted that produced successful outcomes. In a regenerative system, she thought, just calling a halt to a maladapted method allowed natural processes to rise to the surface, setting in motion a complex network of corrective measures to restore balance.

She had arrived the day before and Marshall had met her at the airport. After a leisurely lunch at a small eatery with a seasonal menu featuring locally-grown ingredients, they made their way to the Botanical Gardens. Situated on sixteen acres, there was much of nature to appreciate as spring was announcing her arrival. These gardens featured many plants, shrubs and trees native to the Midwest.

❧

Drew's destination on first returning from Peru was his parents' home. He spent the days unwinding and connecting with Marcy and Jack, resting in the comfort of his former home. He spent hours just walking the woods, surveying the farm and breathing in the spring air. He enjoyed a few lazy days before unpacking and sorting through belongings, what to discard and what to take with him to *Rare Earth*, the farm and Julia – his new home. His time in Peru had taught him to live very simply. He could now afford to include a few extravagances; his mandolin, his telescope and his beloved books would be making the journey north.

It was a time of completion and a time for discarding the old. Most appropriate, he thought; spring cleaning, clearing out the old and bringing in the new. *The Meraki Project* had been an opportunity to hone his leadership skills, leading from a place of humility and inclusiveness. He had partnered with the villagers and gained their respect. He had gained as much knowledge as he had brought to the project. He wondered what it would be like to work side-by-side with Julia, a fusion of work and the personal; she had a passionate nature and a lot of drive.

Drew arrived in late March two days before Lilly and Marshall's arrival. Julia was grateful; two glorious days to themselves, free of clocks, schedules and to freely express their love for each other and celebrate the start of their life together. Julia was planning a ceremony to call in and connect with allies, calling in blessings, seeding the earth with the energy called forth from the star nation, a blessing of their union, their *earthwalk* together. They would close the ceremony with offerings of stones and maple sap placed on the altar expressing gratitude during the season of beginnings and new life emerging.

Drew and Julia basked in the pleasure of being together after months apart. They left unpacking and getting settled for the coming days. Now was the time to indulge in sweet moments; lingering in bed, starting the day with coffee and heartfelt conversation, having abolished time and its usual prescriptives, lost in the moment. Two days in a timeless state and yet it seemed as though they had passed at the speed of light. By noon the next day, Lilly and Marshall arrived setting a new tone and rhythm to their days.

Lilly made the introductions and Marshall greeted everyone with great warmth. He had a way about him that put everyone at ease. He had a way of meeting you where you were, giving you his full attention and staying free of expectation. In his presence, Julia experienced complete acceptance. She wondered what life experiences had brought him to this state. Julia saw the change in her mother; there was a radiance about her. All at once, both their lives were changing significantly, Julia realized.

The pace was casual for the next couple days. There were lively discussions about the shift in consciousness that was taking place around the world, the desire for purpose that seemed to be a common concern for young and old. There were hopeful conversations about equality and new economics.

The leisurely pace was replaced by a flurry of activity in the following days. The sugar house was winding down production as the season came to a close. There were still places in the woods where snow could be gathered, and they invited the students and neighbors for *Sugar on Snow*, a spring tradition. During the last run, the sap evaporated a while longer to a taffy-like consistency. The hot liquid was drawn and carefully poured onto the snow surface gathered in tubs. As the taffy cooled, guests rolled the amber ribbons onto forks. It was a delightful experience usually accompanied by a curious anomaly: playful snowball fights on a warm spring day.

They spent the next two days at The Farm School attending to the Cashmere goats. Drew demonstrated how to use the combs to remove the goats' fine undercoat. Marshall joined the students in gathering the goats, combing out the fiber and releasing them. He got on well with the students, laughing at his first attempts to confine the goats and remove the fiber. It soon became apparent to all that teaming up would produce better results.

The *pashmina* would be washed and carded. The guild had provided drum carders and would be on hand to demonstrate their use. Because the program was just getting under way, the school had decided not to invest in the equipment needed to spin and dye the yarns. They would send the carded fiber to a small company in a neighboring county that would produce the yarn for resale. As the project grew and proved to be profitable, the school would consider going into fiber production. During the coming semester, the Guild members would introduce the dyeing process in a week-long intensive workshop.

The sale of the fiber was an opportunity for the upper-class students to develop a marketing strategy and create a sales platform. The stream of income generated from the sale of the yarn would support the expansion of the program. In time, weaving and spinning classes could be added to the curriculum, initiating a fiber arts program.

They spent the next three days grooming the goats and gathering fiber. Warmer days were on the way and the goats would benefit from being free of their undercoats and the insulation it provided in spite of their temporary objections. Marshall would be leaving the next day. They would miss him. Drew and Marshall had mutual interests and always found plenty to talk about. Julia wished he could extend his stay for the simple pleasure of being in his company. On his last night, he prepared dinner for everyone. He seemed right at home in Lilly's kitchen sharing stories as he poured wine for everyone and turned his attention to dinner's final preparations. It seemed that Marshall was at home wherever he was.

ℒℂ

Julia wanted Drew to feel welcomed. She had cleared one of the bedrooms anticipating Drew would want to set up an office or study. She had left it empty; it would be his space to fill as he chose. He was flattered by her gesture. He brought in a desk and a chair, he put up photos of the Andes, the villagers and the goats. On the opposite wall he put up a *Quechua* tapestry that he had purchased in Pisac. The room remained spacious and airy. It was in need of a rug and Lilly took him to a storage area where some of Catherine's treasured belongings had been stored. He chose a Kilim rug in rich jewel tones, no doubt purchased and brought back from Persia during her travels.

Julia was surprised that Lilly was taking Marshall's departure so calmly. She remained happy and engaged, occupied with meetings with the new students and getting spring planting and the new program underway. There was a new buoyancy in her movements and in her voice as though she was consciously containing her joy. Her mother was in love after years of being on her own.

Lilly observed similar changes in Julia. Her daughter was passionate by nature; it was with effort that she learned to subdue her feelings. Drew's calm presence had a soothing effect on Julia. She seemed to retreat more naturally to a place of reflection, a pause that produced a more encompassing vision. A beautiful synthesis of thought and feeling was then allowed to emerge.

In the weeks that followed, Julia and Drew spent hours in conversation, Julia elaborating on her vision and welcoming Drew's expertise and original ideas. They began prioritizing areas to research and a format for evaluating the merits of potential locations. Once this process was completed, they would invite a group of experts to weigh in on their plans. Julia knew she could count on Drew's objectivity to point out her blind spots. His calm demeanor served as a counterpoint to her passionate nature.

The builders Julia had hired arrived early one April morning; the outdoor living room was about to get underway. She had found a local source for locust that she had milled into two by fours for the framing. She had selected black locust because it is termite and rot resistant and she could avoid the use of treated lumber. The project would be completed in ten days' time. The new addition was situated on the southwestern side of the house. It would benefit from the southern sun and be shaded by the mature tree stand in the west. Julia's plan was to give Catherine's vintage wicker furniture a new life in this space. She had fashioned new cushion seats over the winter and she had repurposed an old iron bed from the attic. Her vision was to spend as much time out of doors as possible. The bedding, granted, would be affected by the weather. For this reason, she had chosen a Murphy bed which would provide additional storage and a dual purpose for the space. She had revised her plan to include two work areas, including desks and access to the internet. She hoped that the outdoor living space would have as much appeal to Drew.

Life was good; she and Drew created a rhythm to their life that was pleasing and that supported them. The day began with morning rituals and meditations. This time was spent outdoors, now that spring was here. In spite of the morning chill, they bundled up, building a fire when necessary and invoked the ancestors, calling in allies from the plant realm, the stone people, the tree spirits and those beings from the realms beyond, asking for guidance and clarification of what actions were needed.

Both enlivened by the elements and focused attention, they then moved into their day, beginning with food preparation and attending to the day's responsibilities. They took turns preparing meals and attending to the chores of the day. The days were punctuated by walks with the dogs, attending to the garden, preparing the ground for annual plantings.

When dinner time arrived, they came together for the evening meal preparations, sharing the day's endeavors and progress. At day's end, they joined again for ceremony thanking the allies who had supported them in their work, assisted them in their relationships and the wisdom they had woven into their day. Both understood that the web of life is rich and fertile, and gratitude creates a bridge and access to all possibilities.

One afternoon, Drew left the house eager to take in the earth's awakening scents and sounds. He and Star headed for the oak grove and the fields beyond. He had never wandered beyond the grove even during his student days. As he reached the edge of the woods, he discovered a pristine pasture slowly coming to life after winter's slumber. He saw red-winged blackbirds perched on fence posts and last season's dry grasses as they heralded spring. He stepped into the midday sun-drenched meadow. In the distance, soft rolling hills gave way to a pine outcropping; at the base of the hill, spring wildflowers grew in the shadow of the pines, the sun having passed its zenith. The air was sweet and cool, the warm breeze intimating about summer days to come.

He walked across the pasture to the edge of the changing terrain. He followed the contour and the rising elevation moving in soft twists and turns and found that the pasture extended far beyond what he had initially taken in. As he walked on, the terrain shifted from pasture to hillside. He moved toward the woods; as he approached, he could hear the sound of water. A stream separated the woods from the pasture. Along the bank, Drew saw a profusion of horsetail remains from last season that would soon be subsumed serving as fodder for new growth as spring advanced and brought warmer days.

Star entered the stream, lapping water and walking across to the other bank. He paused and looked back as if asking Drew if he was coming. Drew paused for a moment his curiosity aroused; he wondered what else might he discover as he continued his exploration. He crossed the stream and joined Star, who had already entered the woods. The white pine grove had obviously been maintained. He found tree stumps near mature trees; this thinning process, no doubt, allowed for more light to reach the forest floor, and support the health of those left to grow. He reached the tree line and looked back; the pasture below was not visible through the density of the woods, but he was able to take in the panorama of the farm. He saw the pond shimmering in the distance, the sugar bush, the unimposing homestead and the school, the mix of deciduous and coniferous trees above rolling hills and broad pastures that were coming to life. He understood at that moment why Catherine had never left once she returned from India. Her stewardship was evident wherever he looked. She had instilled that same love of this land in Lilly and Julia.

He called Star and they slowly made their way down. Returning by the same route, he slowed his pace to take in the old-growth oak grove that Catherine's forebears had valued and preserved. He thought that with the right amount of rain, this could be an excellent place to forage for mushrooms in the coming weeks. The sun was low on the horizon when he returned, content and with a story to share with Julia. He would plan a picnic with Julia and return to this still place on a warm afternoon.

They would return many times; Julia had not been to that distant part of the farm since her childhood. She remembered going there on a horse-drawn wagon entering from the east side of the farm at day's end, at the conclusion of a harvest festival. As she recalled, growing up she had rarely wandered beyond the oak grove because the small meadow within it had captivated her heart and was nearly always her intended destination. Drew expressed his appreciation for this location, its pristine beauty, but remained mysterious about his attachment to it and their frequent visits.

In late May, Drew and Julia felt they were ready to put together a roster of advisors and present their proposal. They planned for a four day-long gathering at the farm and selected several dates to present to the group for their initial meeting. From the onset, they counted on a frank appraisal of the plan and that their advisors would come prepared to offer alternatives. Location was yet to be determined and the group would address possibilities at length.

Paco arrived in April; he was adapting to a new time zone, a new climate and culture shock after many years away from western culture. To Lilly's surprise, within days of his arrival, he offered to teach a hands-on course producing biochar and looking at the impact it had on soil fertility and crop yields. They could set up test plots and compare them to their current methods. Lilly was delighted. They spent the following days planning and selecting challenging sites that would put this method to the test. The focus of the course would be carbon sequestration. Our increased reliance and dependence on fossil fuels for the past fifty years has discharged a massive amount of carbon dioxide into the atmosphere. Coupled with the deforestation that had occurred in the last twenty years, the problem had grown exponentially. Regenerative practices such as introducing cover crops to areas that have been exposed and left bare, a practice of conventional agriculture, would reverse the process by pulling down great amounts of CO_2. Biochar would assist this process.

Conventional farming methods that over time turned living soil to dirt, devoid of humus and microorganisms, had led to desertification. Bare ground meant more CO_2 being released into the atmosphere; a regenerative approach of forest agriculture and reintroducing native plants and grasses would bring back balance.

Lilly had received an invitation to do a presentation for a local environmental organization in its infancy. She extended the invitation to Julia, Drew and Paco; this could be a great opportunity for all three to connect with the local community. Over the course of their young lives, they had learned of and witnessed the degradation of the environment. Predictions of a sixth extinction had been rooted in their upbringing. And yet what they had witnessed was a world unable to stop the momentum toward catastrophe in spite of the pervasive evidence concerning a trajectory set in motion long before they came into being. They each had been called to take an active role in bringing about change.

The assault on nature and its devastating consequences had progressed to the point of awakening many to the mounting evidence that change was needed. Those who had previously been too timid to express what was blatantly obvious, now found their voices. Across the generations, they were being heard. What at first was expressed as a sense of powerlessness and a yearning to avert disaster, became a louder and clearer voice, words spoken with conviction.

Rooted, the local environmental group, was made up of a diverse group of people across many generations. All shared a commitment to the preservation of natural areas, a shift toward renewable energy and to small-scale regenerative agriculture.

Prior to the meeting, Drew, Julia and Paco met to discuss their presentation. Their shared intention was to provide an accurate and honest account of the situation. But foremost, they would present alternatives and supportive evidence that would instill hope and provide incentives to make new informed choices, choices that supported all life.

The disrupted natural cycles that permeated the times they were living in called for calm. Changing how we live was now a necessity and no viable solutions could be found in a state of fear driven by survival emotions. Each had been called in their own way to offer a new way of life, a new way of being. They offered them to those who were ready to entertain other possibilities, a new way of seeing. Change could not be foisted upon others; being receptive to alternatives preceded a shift or change. In other words, change could not be imposed, instead, the need for it required acceptance.

A small reception followed the presentation. The response was enthusiastic and many were eager to implement some of the ideas presented. Some had advocated for change for some time but had not been able to provide a viable plan or workable solutions. The level of expertise that Drew, Julia and Paco had brought to the discussion had raised the group's confidence. The model that had been presented was practical and workable. They were approached about a future consultation as the group got their initial project underway.

Drew, Julia and Paco left the meeting uplifted by the evening's proceedings. All over the world people were rising up, calling for change. A grassroots movement was taking place. With sustained momentum these initial efforts had the potential to transform our relationship with the natural world, with each other and our communities.

Returning home, Lilly greeted them. She invited them to join her outside where she had started a fire. The account of the evening was encouraging, everyone remaining cautiously optimistic. They were reminded to walk their path in humility. Change was always accompanied by resistance and often achieved incrementally. There would be days of hardship; the need for familiarity often produced formidable opposition. Each was committed, all in; they would persist until a way was found.

Lilly had remained outside by the fire after the three young people had left. She admired their youthful and genuine ambitions. They were the new generation coming up; they would avoid the challenges of her time, but they would face new ones undoubtedly. She wondered, could we stand with our feet rooted in the earth reaching for the heavens, and with heartfelt supplication receive and draw down the wisdom of the spheres and pour those blessings at Gaia's feet thus seeding our lives with Infinite Abundance, Infinite Wisdom? The clarion call had been heard by many; how many would stay the course? Dissension was afoot. No real progress could be made in polarization and judgment. This was not to be a time of accounting for our flawed nature, rather it was now time to lift the veil to reveal our magnificence. The way forward was inclusive and open to all. Love was the medicine being offered. Pouring love into the world for the many still living in survival and separation was the only solution going forward. With that thought, she made her way to the house and to bed.

June arrived and the board meeting was upon them. With Lilly and Marshall's help, they had assembled a distinctive advisory board. Passionate and dedicated to their work, each had years of experience behind them. They had known defeats and surmounted professional obstacles. Many had been *the voice in the wilderness* in their chosen fields, pioneers who had been jeered at for advancing ideas that radically departed from long-held sacrosanct assumptions. This put them in a unique position to assess the project with objectivity and provide creative alternatives to impasses. In July, Drew, Julia and Paco would travel west to evaluate the merits and feasibility of a Southwestern location for the project.

The outcome of the meeting surprised them. Their plans had been presented. The comments were supportive yet few evaluations were forthcoming. They were encouraged to forge ahead with their plan. When the panel was questioned about their silence, one member elected to be the spokesperson. The sum of their experience had taught them the importance of plunging in. The obstacles they would face would become their greatest teachers and the process of finding workable alternatives would provide their greatest rewards. The lessons learned would never be forgotten. The confidence gained would fuel their ability to go forward and become the impetus to act on greater ambitions. In the end, Lilly and Marshall who sat on the panel, concurred.

Given the extensive research they had undertaken and the expertise each brought to the project, the panel unanimously predicted a successful outcome. Somewhat dumbstruck, Julia looked at Drew and Paco to gauge their reactions and then turned to the group and thanked them for their participation and the gift of their time.

For Drew, Julia and Paco, the meeting led to more reflection. They spent numerous hours in the following days revisiting their plans. They came together in the evenings after the day's activities and musings to share any new insights. A new sense of excitement seemed to take hold during these gatherings, accompanied by a new sense of freedom. Julia felt more inclined to lean into her heart and not allow her intellect to drive her decisions which led to revisions. Drew felt liberated and was compelled to introduce new applications that had yet to be tested or tried. Paco had been reluctant to share his ideas about the Commons but was now ready to present them.

The Journey West

They'd opted to travel to New Mexico by train. They had been hard at work for the past few months and the train ensured a leisurely pace, giving them the chance to turn their attention to relaxation and play. The train afforded unique vistas through untrammeled areas. They talked, read and dozed, often lulled by the movement of the train. On their second day of travel, Julia fell asleep gazing out the window. As she came to, she gazed out at the high desert. Among the muted green sagebrush, she spotted desert marigolds, scarlet pimpernel, saltbrush and chicory.

The importance of place in the overall design of a regenerative system suddenly assaulted her. She sat up more alert. She was struck with the clarity that place was central to the success of any design and called for place-appropriate practices. A place needed to be seen as unique, to be viewed holistically; its strengths and weaknesses as part of a whole. Having identified its strengths and vigor, a plan could be initiated that supported the system's weakest area to create a thriving ecosystem. To do otherwise was to overlook the value of unique traits and their contribution to the whole.

Looking up, Drew noticed that Julia seemed more alert. He sensed that she was deep in thought. He smiled at her, but she did not notice; he went back to his book. Her enthusiasm for sharing new ideas and insights would no doubt lead to a conversation when the time was right.

Julia suddenly understood that this way of apprehending the natural world paved the way to seeing humankind through that generous lens, from a place of wholeness, without disparity; no breakdown of the whole into parts, abolishing what had previously been deemed attractive and acceptable and what might be assessed as needing reform.

Relationships would engender respect, measured in terms of unique characteristics and value. She could imagine the impact such a change would have on society as a whole and how it would affect business and economics. Support, goodwill and purpose would become the foundations on which all human transactions would operate. If these values were the substrata informing commerce, they would naturally mitigate imbalance and excess. By supporting the very best in people, the very least in their character would inevitably be lifted.

Julia noticed that the train was slowing and would soon come to a stop. They had arrived in Albuquerque, New Mexico. They would be staying here for the night before traveling north. They made their way to baggage claim before making their way to the youth hostel. In the previous months, they had identified several small companies who were involved with promoting and implementing regenerative agriculture in New Mexico. They had selected some well-established projects that the three could visit and evaluate the merits of permaculture in the Southwest Desert.

ↂ

Marshall had become a frequent visitor since his initial visit in March. He and Lilly knew where this was headed but neither were in need of a decision or a permanent arrangement at this point. Lilly had offered him the yurt as an office space; he had accepted and while the trio was away, he and Lilly had converted the space to meet his needs. They were both eager to hear the outcome of the trip out west. Whatever the outcome, they would offer support.

A New Vision, A New Reality

A year had passed since the trip to New Mexico. They had launched the project in early June. In the end, the back meadow on the farm had been selected as the village site. After returning from New Mexico, Drew had insisted on taking Julia and Paco to this favorite location. In light of their recent travels and discoveries, he had asked them to envision the village from this site. They had camped on the land for days becoming intimately acquainted with it; the terrain, the location, the flora and the fauna. At dusk, they watched the deer visiting the stream and as light faded to dark, listened to the calls of the Great Horned owls. During the day, the air was filled with birdsong. The two dominant habitats – meadow and woodland – contributed to the great diversity of species that called this place their home. The native plants of the meadow attracted bees, dragonflies and butterflies. They had to become part of the landscape if they hoped to become observers of the teeming life around them.

For those few days, sitting quietly for hours became the normal course of life.

They noted that the wind came from the Northwest in July. They identified areas where moisture was plentiful, dry areas and areas with poor drainage, the flora affirming these patterns. After several days, they left feeling intimately connected to the land having established a sense of place. They repeated this process in the fall, during the winter and then again in the spring, noticing the nuances and changes each season presented.

Through the woods, the deer trails became more visible once the leaves had fallen. Beechnut husks littered the ground and partridge berry vines were easily spotted on the wooded trails bearing shiny red berries nestled in evergreen leaves confined to the ground. The stream was nearly completely frozen during the winter and the snow covering the meadow drifted creating repetitive patterns crafted by the prevailing winds. In the spring, the wooded hillside was covered with trillium and ramps with bluets and spring beauties strewn across the meadow. These observations helped them identify the traits and potential of the place. Once a decision was made, they returned for a ceremony to request permission from the ancestors and spirits of the land to become its occupants and its stewards.

ᐯ

Lilly had deeded over fifty-five acres to Julia. She would hold the land in perpetual trust and create a private home ownership collective that required active participation of its residents. The owners would pay for their homes situated on generous parcels with *in perpetua* land use. Should a community member decide to leave, the home would be purchased with a predetermined assigned value so that homes could remain affordable to future community members.

The legal documents including a unique covenant took some months to draft and approve. The overarching sentiment was that all community members' interest had been thoughtfully considered and those who joined were committed and in agreement with the principles on which the community was founded.

In New Mexico, Drew, Julia and Paco had visited many ambitious and successful projects. Because of the arid climate and sparse rainfall, a large emphasis was placed on water conservation. Cisterns, rain barrels to capture runoff, and grey water systems that included man-made ponds dominated the overall designs. Swales were frequently put to use. Every possible water conservation feature was employed. Grasses and fruit varieties that were drought resistant were important features of their designs. Both wind and solar energy were abundantly available. The dry climate was well-suited to cobb and adobe construction. A progressive western mindset played favorably in the future development of regenerative systems. As newcomers, they would have to purchase a large tract of land, meet with local authorities and ascertain building restrictions, establish relationships and procure financing for an unconventional project.

The return trip had given each of them time to reflect and consider both locations. It became clear to Drew that *Rare Earth*, the farm, the school and the land were assets that would make a huge contribution to the success of the project. It had motivated him to initiate a visit to the expansive meadow in the days following their return. The gift of the land and the countless resources associated with the farm were huge assets and would support and expedite the project getting underway.

Drew had been pleasantly surprised that making a pitch for this location was unnecessary. As they made their way to the meadow with tents and supplies, he had sensed in the silence that both Paco and Julia had read his mind and were seeing the location with fresh eyes.

ᑫᓄ

During the past year, Drew and Julia had become increasingly involved with *Rooted*, the local environmental organization in town. Among them were members interested in joining the village community. Lilly had announced the launching of the community some months earlier on her weekly *Rare Earth* blog. Several alumni expressed an interest in joining the community. Some elected to come for a closer look and to get a greater understanding of the project. Three young couples from the nearby university were also interested in joining. They anticipated that a vibrant community with a new vision would be an ideal place to raise their young families. A retired couple had contacted Julia; they had recently returned from Germany after life-long careers in academics. They were attracted to joining a multi-generational community.

The development would need to evolve carefully and would require educating the community. A group of interested members met once a month at the farm. Drew, Paco and Julia took turns leading meetings to explain the level of commitment that would be required of community members, from manual labor to decision-making to learning many new skills. Lilly and Marshall also contributed lectures on a multi-tiered approach to water conservation and renewable energy. The community website provided information online with topics ranging from community-based economics including gifting and shared resources, practicing voluntary simplicity, alternative housing construction, creating a forest garden, local purchasing, and other inspiring content that encouraged viewing nature in all its diversity as more than a commodity.

The newcomers were encouraged to spend time on the land to become acquainted with it. Some set up tents and spent days exploring beyond the rolling meadows and nearby woods, taking in the breadth of the farm. The village location was bordered on all sides by well-tended acres, woods and the school. The consensus was that the farm itself made the village that much more attractive. Its resources would be widely utilized by the residents. Those who were ready to join began to explore the land for possible home sites. Some arrived at the monthly meetings with house plans asking for input. There was a great sense of excitement as spring approached.

Paco became a faculty member at *Rare Earth*. The hands-on biochar course he taught when he first arrived was a huge success. This had led to a course on trees, their great contribution to carbon sequestration and the impact of deforestation. He spent some time exploring the often-overlooked health benefits of trees. Intensive research was still needed in this area and Paco's hope was to inspire a few recruits who could turn their attention to pioneering research. He started a small pilot program to identify some of the oldest trees in the area and clone them. His attention was particularly focused on old growth walnut, native to this area. These would initially become available to village members to shade their homes, mitigate the effects of wind and contribute to the overall health of the ecosystem and all its occupants.

The following semester, Paco offered an advanced version of the course. He had mapped out a landscape plan for the village commons including walnut, beech, maple, locust and hickory. The second tier would feature varieties of apple, peach and plum trees. Fruiting ornamental shrubs would make up the last tier, attracting birds and insects. The students who were enrolled were paired into teams and their final project was to come up with alternative plans. The course content would pave the way for making good design decisions. The village stood to gain a great deal from the school's research. Relationships between the school and the village were already evolving. The students enrolled in the Regenerative Building Program had submitted designs during one of the monthly meetings and with the supervision of the head of the program, they were meeting with members to adapt and modify designs to fit the needs and aesthetic of those interested. Lilly, Marshall, Drew and Paco, the permaculture team, were well-equipped to provide the expertise needed as members began planning the development of their home sites.

∽

Julia lay in bed next to Drew barely awake. It was spring and the first village habitats would soon be going up. A shift happened for Julia once the location had been decided. She became more relaxed and playful and imagination became a better part of her planning moving forward. As she lay in bed reflecting, she could hear Drew's soft rhythmic breathing. She was enjoying this quiet time before jumping into action. As she relaxed next to Drew, a childhood memory floated up; she remembered that she had gone to bed and had been unable to fall asleep. She recalled her thoughts drifting to the Great Mystery around her. She'd wondered, could she be merely a speck in God's being? She imagined herself as God. She had suddenly felt so immense that she had opened her eyes to make sure she was still contained within her child body.

She reflected that after the many months of hard work, she and Drew felt gratified by the interest that the village project was attracting. Julia would be lecturing on Vedic Architecture at the upcoming monthly meeting. She wanted to explore these ancient principles and broaden the scope of potential options. Each month house plans were being presented and evaluated. This gave the members food for thought before making a final decision on their house plans. Drew stirred and opened his eyes; smiling, he reached out to her. The day was already feeling very promising.

❧

Marshall had surprised Julia and Drew one morning with the plans for his and Lilly's home. They had selected a parcel at the edge of the stream and wooded hills facing north. The house design exuded the philosophy that small is beautiful. It was a charming cobb house that utilized thermal mass to assist with cooling and heating. The English style home featured rounded walls and included an effective recycling water system that maximized reuse. The design featured many windows, a fireplace and multi-purpose rooms. They planned to access the stream to create a series of small ponds to capture runoff naturally and reduce their water consumption for the forest garden Marshall had designed.

Julia and Drew were enjoying a more relaxing pace. There were still many responsibilities to attend to as the project moved forward, but enjoyment had replaced the urgency of the previous months. The days' activities seemed to energize them. They came home ready to enjoy the aspects of their personal lives.

Two *Rare Earth* alumni had elected to build tiny houses; Patrick had designed his home to include two retractable rounded bay windows to enlarge the inside space of his tiny house design. He had located a source of recycled cedar and he had decided on board and batten construction for the outside. The house would be finished in a deep blue pigment with white framed windows. Patrick's plan included recycled wood floors, upcycled granite remnants from a construction site for kitchen and bathroom counter tops. His biggest investment was the purchase of uPVC windows, and he had decided on a geosolar system to cool & heat his home. Others considering building a tiny house were eager to learn of Patrick's plans in more detail.

The retired professors had decided on a container home constructed from retired rail cars. It was two stories high and included many south facing windows and skylights on their sloping roof. The container on the second floor was positioned perpendicular to the lower level and created a spacious covered outdoor space facing east. It would be framed and screened to maximize the use of the outdoor space and featured a fireplace. The students at *Rare Earth* had been instrumental in guiding the final design to insure maximum efficiency and a supportive interior environment. They were searching far and wide to locate as many recycled materials as possible for the interior construction.

The Lasetters were a family with two young children. They designed a bamboo home. The design was a fusion of both Asian and contemporary architecture. The floor plan was canted at angles which gave the home interest and a sense of containment. Much of the interior was to be finished with light natural woods reaching up into the rafters of the vaulted ceiling in parts of the house. A rooftop gable extended above the roof line with windows on four sides adding light to the house and allowing heat to escape in summer by venting the windows. Dormers were introduced by cutting away a wedge of roof and inserting uPVC windows. A wall of windows faced the front of the house that was protected from temperature variability by the extended porch that wrapped around the front of the house. There was a pond in front of the house routed from the stream and once having watered the surrounding landscape the water was returned to the stream. Flowering crabapple trees, fruiting apple and nut trees were planted on one side; the back faced the stream and overlooked the wooded hillside. The Southeastern portion nearest the house was designated for annual gardens bordered by a variety of bush berries and a nearby shed. Next year, the newest members, the Emersons, would arrive from the Northeast in early spring to build their straw bale home.

Terra Bella

The time for the first home construction was approaching. It seemed appropriate to plan a ceremony to thank the land, to make offerings and celebrate the start of a new vision and a new community. The celebration was lively with abundant offerings of food, music, dance and laughter. The mood was bright with the realization that their ideas and intentions, their well-thought-out plans were about to take shape and become tangible. The first labyrinth had been constructed and became the site of the celebration. The day-long event began with a tobacco ceremony, calling in the directions and the allies. Everyone was invited to walk the labyrinth, dispelling any concerns and doubts as they walked to the center and returning with a clear vision for the land, the community and their own personal journey.

An entrance and road had been created linking the village to the main road. The road was serpentine in design to maintain privacy, minimize the removal of trees and create interest. A metal gate designed and created by one of the members had been erected. A leaf pattern with pendant flowers dominated the design. An earth-rammed curved wall had been constructed flanking each side of the gate. Mortar, colored with autumn-green pigment, had been applied to the wall and the name of the community had been mounted in hand-crafted letters which had been cut in wood and wrapped with hammered brass. The wall remained covered; the project now complete would be revealed today as part of the celebration.

After a community breakfast of griddle cakes and maple syrup, eggs, seasonal fruit and farm-raised and farm-made sausage, everyone made their way to the yurt that had been erected for the duration of the upcoming construction. Tables were set up around the periphery of the room and on both the walls and the tables drawings of the homes slated for construction were displayed. There was an area designated for house plans from the *Rare Earth Regenerative Home Design* students, food for thought for those still deciding. Next, neighbors walked the land inviting members to share details of their plans, the placement of the home, the features unique to their location and what inspirations had driven their design.

The unveiling of the village gate was scheduled after lunch. Children, dogs and adults boisterously made their way up the drive, the gate not visible until the last turn. The excitement was palpable. Four of the men had made their way ahead of the group and set up ladders. At the appointed time, they would remove the tarps covering the wall. The crowd made their way across a footbridge that crossed the nearby creek bed so the gathering would witness the unveiling standing outside the gate. One member had brought a trumpet and with a bit of fanfare got everyone's attention. The tarps were lowered to reveal a distressed metal gate representing flowering branches of honey locust. The letters on the wall read *Terra Bella.* Everyone cheered and clapped. The reality of the village was taking shape. Marshall had seen to it that champagne on ice and sparkling juice were brought to the gate in a wagon so a toast could be offered. After the toast, the gates were opened and the group made its way through returning to the village center where the celebration would continue.

The local paper had been invited for the unveiling of the gate. A photo made its way onto the front page of the paper the next day with a caption forecasting a new era. The story that followed had been well researched and written in flattering terms. *Rare Earth* had received accolades over the years and earned the respect of the community. Both Catherine and Lilly had developed and maintained a relationship with town officials. Its reputation had eased the way for the legal and logistical negotiations that the village presented. Any objections to unprecedented procedures were dealt with objectively and without undue resistance.

Julia and Drew made their way back home, walking in the dark, feeling giddy and content. The dogs led the way and kept them to the trail. For them, the celebration was the culmination of their efforts to date. Both walked away from the festivities having witnessed commitment from the community; the genuine interest shown for each other's plans, the labor they had volunteered and the skills shared. Both were greatly encouraged. They walked home holding hands occasionally glancing at one another, each feeling a sense of gratification and gratitude.

Patrick's tiny house would be the first home on the land, with construction scheduled just days after the celebration. The mood had carried over and the event created great excitement; in spite of the novel design ideas he had included, the house was finished in ten days' time. The Regenerative Home Design students had volunteered to help to gain experience, the community members also pitched in during their free time, and the Farm School had signed up a group of volunteers. The whole effort made everyone realize the power of many hands and many skills, the sense of reward that grew from collaboration and giving.

Julia and Drew's house was scheduled for construction the following summer. There were too many projects to oversee with village life in its infancy to consider it now. In the end, they had fused two architectural styles; a Biotecture model adding Vedic principles of astrology and paying close attention to the purpose of the rooms, situating them in appropriate directions to maximize the well-being and prosperity of its occupants.

❦

When Lilly met Marshall, it was as if the story of her life had come to an end, as though the rivers and estuaries that carried her past had emptied into a vast sea. She loved Marshall with a freedom she had never known before. He did not need to show up in a particular way, he did not need to fulfill any strident hopes or needs. The river of life was quietly flowing, in perfection, as it was. She was both empty and full. The emptiness gave rise to great beauty, boundless gratitude, great peace. Free of all longing, life was a gift. In the absence of grasping, one beautiful moment slipped past replaced by another. She found no words to express her new state of being. She had simply arrived; free of history, free to love everything and every moment, not Marshall more than her students, her daughter more than the presence of the sun. She knew one love. Marshall had been the catalyst.

It was not what Marshall said or the credo he followed that made his presence such a gift. He possessed a wise and generous spirit whose virtue relied on an economy of words. He lived the wisdom that he had gathered and that informed his life. He was curious, thoughtful and kind. Wherever life had taken him, he had learned to cross the bridge to that vast impersonal universe where the human experience was but a fragment of what one might apprehend and know. His calm disposition was attractive by nature. He had an uncanny way of disarming anyone he came in contact with; everyone was welcomed.

Peace wove through Lilly's days like gossamer, infused with lightness and contentment. She had never felt so grounded or so buoyant. She often thought of Catherine; this precious state had been familiar to her. This sudden recognition brought Lilly joy. Elation was a province whose air was too rarefied, she thought; peace lay at the epicenter, why wander? She loved every moment of her life. Hardship, loneliness, loss, grief, they had brought her to that moment, rendered her malleable and ready to surrender, surrender to *All That Is*. This is what Marshall's presence brought to every moment they shared; an unspoken quiet joy permeated every cell of his being and now hers.

When Marshall came to stay, they fell into a rhythm that did not require negotiations. Without effort, life fell into place. After years alone, she would have never guessed that such a seamless transition was possible. Planning the house was a pleasurable experience for both of them. They formed a vision and began shaping it. At the end of the day, Marshall walked Lilly to the drafting table to share his progress and new ideas. The next morning, Marshall would find articles, photos and hand-sketched drawings in an email from Lilly. That night, he usually had new drawings and a variety of options incorporating what had been most inspiring from her communication. Soon, Marshall responded with similar findings that found their way into her inbox; they were both humored by this correspondence.

In time, they arrived at a design neither could have imagined alone. The kitchen was magnificent, the centerpiece of the house. Both loved to cook, so creating an efficient kitchen in a modest space was a worthy challenge and Marshall had succeeded. He'd added a pantry that was tall and narrow in the final drawings as a surprise for Lilly. Their home was scheduled for construction in late summer. The second-year students would be returning in late August and were eager to assist. If they stayed on schedule, the house would be finished in mid-December.

Lilly had just learned that she had been selected as the recipient of a prestigious award in honor of her thirty years of pioneering work in Regenerative Agriculture. She would be traveling to Seattle to give a speech and receive the award in early November.

The fall crops were in and the activity on the farm was winding down. The grey days of November had arrived, the oaks stubbornly holding on to brown leaves that rattled in the cold breeze. Lilly was making her way to the meadow to survey the progress of their home. The project had gotten underway in mid-October. She wondered if she would see a noticeable change on their return from Seattle.

Lilly would be traveling with her family; Paco and a couple staff members would also be attending the award ceremony. They were leaving the next day. Lilly was not one to bring attention to herself; she was at first resistant to traveling with what seemed like a large entourage. She relented realizing that they were eager to celebrate her accomplishments. They arrived in Seattle early and spent a couple days exploring the city. Marshall had planned for a dinner celebration the evening prior to the award ceremony.

The next day, they arrived early and made their way to the hall where the presentation was to be held. Lilly and her guests were seated in the front row near the stage as people began to file in and find seats. When the time came, Lilly climbed the steps, made her way to the podium and delivered her speech:

This gathering this afternoon is intended to honor my contribution to the life sciences, but I prefer to think of it as the science of living. I am deeply honored to be here.

Water is alive and intelligent as are the wind, the trees, rocks and soil, each an individuated emanation formed from billion-year-old carbon. These forms are animated with the same intelligence that created the magnificent and complex form that we experience as being human. The endless processes that go on within us without our prompting or volition are the workings of a universe onto itself. We often fail to fully comprehend what a marvel of creation we are.

With the sun's assistance water is transformed to vapor which rises forming clouds and then carried by the wind, sometimes for thousands of miles before it is precipitated onto new soil and a new environment. It nourishes life indiscriminately.

Trees do not live independently. They create communities, connected by an underground web, their means of communicating and sharing. Their root system is a network, a communication system. They alert one another of imminent danger; they share nutrients to support the life of one in need; they direct this support through this lifeline with intention and purpose in order to sustain the health of their community. In this way, cooperation guarantees a thriving environment. This inviolable agreement is sadly missing from human relationships and enterprise.

Our journey during the last few hundred years has taken us off course. Our deeper intelligence has been obscured and overruled; we have lost our intuitive guiding system. Our desire for ease has led to choices that have compromised our physical, emotional, psychological and spiritual health. We are afflicted by our never-ending need for comfort, convenience and perpetual expansion. We ignored those who cautioned about the long-term costs to both the natural world we live in and our own well-being. Nature's resources were considered boundless and ours to appropriate. With the advent of the industrial age, we blindly foreclosed on our stewardship to the earth. We have defiled what is sacred by reducing this natural abundance to commodities and resources. And still Gaia forgives us.

How can we hope to be healed, to be supported when we defile the intelligent life surrounding us, the source from which our lives and well-being depend? The answers we seek are everywhere around us and must be sought in alert and quiet observation. We are infants on this timeline of evolution. We have become misguided marauders. The evidence is all around us.

Biomimicry has much to offer us as a path to healing. In asking our precursors with billions of years of evolution behind them to in—form us, we humble ourselves and *take our place as the relative newcomers that we are. This humble act holds the potential to heal our relationship with the natural world, to shift to a cooperative and participatory relationship and the possibility of creating heaven here on earth.*

Nature has been my teacher; she has taught me that diversity and abundance are innate traits that insure continuity. Nature relies on a complex yet delicate system dependent on cooperation and an understanding and respect for the carrying capacity of its interconnected and diverse resources. Working within these confines, all of nature thrives. In a language that humans can understand, this is Divine Generosity, the joy of Creation wanting to keep this process alive in ever-growing cycles of expression, adaptation and renewal.

These cycles informed our predecessors for millennia; they were understood and revered. Over time a breach occurred, our connection severed. Domination and separation followed, setting in motion the disintegration we now witness. Vital cycles have been broken and we too are broken. At the deepest level, the unidentified sense of foreboding and anxiety so prevalent in society speaks to the malaise we are all feeling. What we crave is connection, a wholesome association with all that lives, a movement toward wholeness.

Do the luxuries and so-called time-saving technologies that contemporary life foists upon us offset the pressure and demands put on our time? Have we gained a meaningful degree of freedom or are we enslaved by what we have been told are indispensable necessities? Has technology created more freedom or bred another form of dependence?

The overwhelming evidence that we are at a turning point, that we are at the precipice of the sixth major extinction gives us pause to consider choosing a different path. Deforestation, climate change, enormous loss of species and the world-wide health crises have for many of us had a sobering effect. We can no longer turn the other way. It is time to learn what it means to be human, that we are active participants in the Great Web of Life. Consider these words from Einstein: 'We are slowed down sound and light waves, a walking bundle of frequencies tuned into the cosmos. We are souls dressed up in sacred biochemical garments and our bodies are the instruments through which our souls play their music.' These words were written nearly one hundred years ago and have reached a few. They have yet to be entertained or understood by the majority.

Humanity operates at a frequency level, an octave of possibilities that informs our perceptions and choices. Throughout history, mankind has experienced significant shifts that have profoundly altered our perception. Some shifts contributed to the expansion of our minds, bringing freedom, the opportunity for contemplation and fueling

233

greater understanding and innovation; some created cycles of harmony and wholeness while others led us toward destruction and dissonance. In and of themselves, these shifts can be seen as advancements, but our consummate myopia rarely has allowed for a more expansive and comprehensive view. We are multidimensional beings who are being called to expand beyond our three-dimensional constructs and constraints, to move beyond fear, greed, unbridled power and separation.

For centuries our existence has been driven by the work ethic. Society has promoted productivity as the hallmark of civilization and we unquestioningly have marched to its drum and consequently derived our sense of self from our outer accomplishments and acquisitions. Yet our souls cry out for wholeness and freedom. Entrenched in lives devoted to duty, lives that often lack passion, to question it for most, evokes feelings of guilt and shame. When this undisputed premise is questioned at a youthful age, it is labeled as the folly of youth, most eventually giving in to its overwhelming authority. The bravest among us, walk away.

A shift is occurring, pulling us toward balance. The time has arrived to relinquish age-old patterns which stifle creativity, well-being and joy. Some societies have readily embraced this change and provide a model for a more humane approach to commerce. Societies that provide more free time and encourage connection and relaxation have demonstrated greater productivity and ingenuity. Working in groups, ideas flourish. The greatest inspirations often arrive when relaxing into a simple state of being without agenda or expectation. Energy restored, filled with enthusiasm and original ideas, one can accomplish in a few hours what would have taken days or weeks of effort primed by duty.

Within nature, there are seasons within seasons. As we tune in to those natural rhythms, we discover our unique rhythms because we ARE nature, not separate from it. Each day is new when approached with curiosity and open to possibilities. For decades we have been warned by visionaries among them E F Schumacher, Wendell Berry and Rachel Carson. In recent times, we've gained the knowledge of E O Wilson, Janine Benyus, Diana Beresford-Kroeger, Charles Eisenstein and the vision of countless others, men and women who have devoted their lives to finding ways to return to living as a harmonious whole.

In the words of Waorani leader, Nemonte Nenquimo, "we are a people that knows too little and wields too much power." A time for humility and evaluation is much needed and long overdue. And in spite of the perils that loom before us, there is life yet to be. We need to establish and cultivate relationships with the indigenous cultures that have persisted in spite of our efforts to eliminate their cultures and way of life. They have much to teach us *about maintaining a balanced relationship with nature. Often seen as primitive, we have failed to recognize the sophistication and wisdom woven within their traditions. We are designed to be in nature; it is our home. This simple shift has the power to restore our health, shift our perceptions and set changes in motion that reflect a newfound respect for the natural world.*

There are those among us who were inspired by the pioneers of the ecological movement who have held to a vision, some investing years working with indigenous cultures in developing innovative solutions and in spite of opposition, we have held fast to our convictions. The time for implementation on a massive scale is at hand. Nature, our greatest source of wisdom, supports our very lives.

We need transparency in business and economic affairs. We need an economic system that serves people first and foremost. We are being called to reconnect with our innate nature; to rely on the heart as well as the mind, to pause and to listen. To wait long enough for the inner voice to offer guidance, new ways of seeing the world both within us and without. Our current economic system operates without heart or soul, designed for the gain of the few. It is a system obsessed with gain and never-ending expansion, based on a cold calculus that excludes human worth and freedom from strife. Thus fragmented, how can we hope to create a world where peace and contentment become possible if all cannot have equal access to resources that meet common needs?

Lilly went on to speak of *Rare Earth* and the inquiry process that was the foundation on which the school rested. New ideas were always encouraged and explored to assess their merits. Failures often proved to be the ground for further exploration, intuition often guiding innovation. Everyone was encouraged to become immersed in nature, to seek solutions through observation. She learned as much from those in attendance as they learned from her. In the end, collaboration proved to be the most effective means of fostering invention. She concluded:

In the beginning everything is in balance. We must learn how to maintain that balance. If you are unsure, then do nothing. Wait. Wait for the answers and then live the answers. The Ancient Knowers have held consciousness for humanity for eons; they have held the medicine that keeps the world whole. We are now being asked to assume our role, to climb the next rung in our evolution. We must rejoin nature, return and be guided by Natural Law.

With these final words, she stepped away from the podium. Her family and friends were moved by the strength of her message. As she stepped off the stage after the presentation of the award, each greeted her with unspoken appreciation; she saw it in their gaze, she felt it in their touch. For Lilly there was much to celebrate; the award ceremony was over, the focus was no longer on her. They were going home, to a new chapter of their lives. They will celebrate Winter Solstice in their new home in a few short weeks.

❧

Two years have passed since the unveiling of the village gate. The village is now made up of twenty-three homes with five more scheduled for construction this coming summer. Drew and Julia are now situated in their new home in the village; they are expecting their first child in the fall. An economic center is beginning to take shape. Some businesses operate from their homes; others have added small studio sheds to accommodate their needs and still others are choosing more visibility in a low-profile business district that Drew has designed with Marshall's vision and assistance. Folks from town make their way to the village to access the unique services and frequent the small eateries that have been established. *Terra Bella* launched a farmers market the first year and people throughout the county are frequenting their Saturday morning market. Others have joined the community CSA. Village tours are frequently offered as interest in learning about the community is growing. The village community has decided to build two new tiny houses and three studio sheds for guests who want an extended stay at *Terra Bella.* The community has generated a great deal of interest and people throughout the States and Canada are requesting workshops and information on how to replicate their efforts.

Visitors are required to leave their cars at the gate; an electric-powered bus offers service to the village center. The work-exchange bank that Julia established is a great success and overall people in the community work fewer hours and spend more time devoted to what matters most: community, family, learning and play.

Paco, with the help of his students, has created The Village Commons which is the backdrop for the business district. At the heart of it, the Common House was erected, taking shape over the course of the summer months. It houses a multi-purpose gathering space designed for lectures, conferences and meetings. It is easily transformed into a banquet facility and adjoins the community kitchen. The kitchen provides energy-efficient state-of-the-art equipment for food processing. Food-based community ventures rent the space for production. Community members schedule time for food preserving and community meals.

Since Julia and Drew moved into their new home, Catherine's home has been transformed into a guest house. Bathed in morning light, her library remains intact and is a favorite spot where guests often linger perusing her extensive book collection. Her reading chair and desk remain in the room. Her spirit still inhabits the room, no doubt a real benefit to all those who sit quietly reading or contemplating.

ᏉᎾ

A week from now, the community will host a Thanksgiving meal for the community at large. The celebration was conceived to express gratitude and provide meals for those unable to provide for themselves. The community has put together gift bags that include seasonal foods, toiletries, blankets and health care appointments to support those in need, and will be handed out as the guests leave. Thanksgiving will be a potlatch celebration, the givers receiving infinitely more than their material offerings. In this way, a spirit of generosity and hospitality will extend beyond the boundaries of *Terra Bella* and ripple out into the community at large. The gates to the village remain open at all times.

The village has a foundation to rest upon yet will remain largely improvisational. The principles it rests upon deem it so. Its very fabric rests on fluidity and adaptability. New expressions of deeply-rooted truths will emerge in a new lexicon. They will be entertained and implemented after contemplation has disclosed their merits, the benefits to the whole evaluated, the whole of nature considered.

Consideration will extend beyond the whim of the moment, the ease it might provide, the disconnect it might engender. If unity is the community's primary intention then a return to the contextual is called for in all aspects of village life; every thought, idea, innovation entertained within the framework of the whole, a web connecting *every* thing. This new era is an experiment; the intention driving this experiment is a return to wholeness, an awareness of spirit within all matter. It calls for the dismantling of separation, abolishing compartmentalization and division. It relies on the synergy of complexity and its fluid workings, the dynamic flow of reciprocity and a cornucopia of possibilities.

Growth never occurs in a straight line or a predetermined trajectory. No destination was ever reached without obstacles or deviations. The old story will persist supplanted by a degree of melancholy, doubt and resistance until a new path is firmly established. The village will no doubt go through growing pains; each challenge will provide opportunities to expand problem solving skills and to experience greater resilience. Some community members will be here for a while and move on, while others will remain for the long run and newcomers will be welcomed. In the absence of judgment, the community, a living organism, can undergo change, adjusting and adapting without the fealty of permanence. The world is shifting and expanding as it always has and will. The interplay between the macrocosm and the microcosm can no longer be denied.

Julia, Drew, Paco, Lilly and Marshall came together and created a vision, investing it with their love, talents, gifts and energies. Others joined them, bringing it to life. The founders provided the fuel needed to bring it into form. Their individual investments to breathe life into its creation is now behind them; they are community members each with a voice among the many. Sovereignty and freedom live side by side, welcomed by everyone.

"Chickpea to Cook"

Jalal ad-Din Muhammad Rumi

Translation By Coleman Barks

A Chickpea leaps almost over the rim of
the pot where it's being boiled.
"Why are you doing this to me?"
The cook knocks him down with the ladle.
"Don't try to jump out. You think I'm
torturing you. I'm giving you flavor.
So you can mix with spices and rice and be
the lovely vitality of a human being.
Remember when you drank rain in
the garden? That was for this.
Grace first. Sexual pleasure, then a boiling new life
begins and the Friend has something good to eat."

Eventually the chickpea will say to the cook,
"Boil me some more. Hit me with the skimming
spoon. I can't do this by myself. I'm like
An elephant who dreams of gardens back in
Hindustan and doesn't pay attention to his driver.

You're my cook, my driver, my way into
existence. I love your cooking."

The cook says, "I was once like you, fresh from the
ground. Then I boiled in time, and boiled in the body,
two fierce boilings. My animal soul grew powerful. I
controlled it with practices, and boiled some more, and
boiled once beyond that and became your teacher."

Acknowledgements

No book can ever be entirely credited to its author. Each day we are influenced by the world around us, where our steps lead us and the sage words and understanding that make their way into our experience be it nature's kaleidoscope or the curiosity and genius of humanity. To that end, I wish to acknowledge those who have unknowingly provided and informed my perceptions and my written words.

I wish to thank Nassim Haramein for his relentless research and pursuit to broaden our understanding and to show us the Wider Intelligent World we live in beyond what we have been able to imagine and entertain to date. To Marshall Lefferts for his seminal work *Cosmometry: Exploring the HoloFractal Nature of the Cosmos*. The pioneering work of Benoit Mandelbrot, his discovery of the fractal geometry of nature. Buckminster Fuller who dedicated his life to discovering nature's building principles. To all the brave souls past and present who dare to challenge cherished beliefs and look beyond our current understanding of the nature of reality. Each new discovery confirms the Innate Intelligence which is the scaffolding of All That Is. Much of this process is initiated with *What If* questions.

I wish to thank one of my cherished American heroes, Wendell Berry, for his tireless efforts over the course of several decades of bringing awareness to the impact of our indiscriminate social and economic changes and their effects on our eroded American landscape. Among those who in recent times offer regenerative solutions, I wish to thank Bill Mollison for introducing us to permaculture, Eliot Coleman for showing me that harsh climate conditions need not limit the growing season and Toby Hemenway. *Gaia's Garden* was my introduction to permaculture principles and its applications.

I am grateful to Jim Robbins for *The Man Who Planted Trees* and thus introducing me to David Milarch's work, the work of Diana Beresford-Kroeger, Lou Licht and countless others who have dedicated their lives to finding solutions within nature and nature's cycles to co-opt the inevitable decline and destruction created by the myopic implementation of methods that resulted in the wholesale degradation of our soils, waterways, forests and environment. Many thanks to Janine Benyus for her contribution to the evolution of Biomimicry, for Ask Nature and the Biomimicry Institute and the many who have joined her in promoting nature-based and inspired solutions to innovation and problem solving.

Julia's visit to Ontario and the *bioplan* she implements at *Terra Bella* represent the work and research of Diana Beresford-Kroeger as presented in *The Man Who Planted Trees*, Jim Robbins; Spiegel & Grau. New York. 2015. *Trees Hold the Answers to Many of Life's Problems*, Diana Beresford-Kroeger,

Globe and Mail, September 2019. The implementation of a willow and poplar forest for the purpose of sewage treatment in the village of *Terra Bella*, is the brainchild of Lou Licht of Ecolotree. It is a technique sometimes referred to as phytore-mediation, a form of ecotechnology.

The concept of rendering the word information as in-formation as it appears within the text, was adapted from Marshall Lefferts book, *Cosmometry*, I believe that entertaining it in this way gives new meaning to this word.

The menu for the Andean feast was sourced from *Traditional High Andean Cuisine: Allin Mukuy* and *Sumak Mikuy*, published by Food and Agriculture Organization of the United Nations.

The information on Cashmere goats was inspired by Lani Malmberg of Green Goat LLC located in Colorado. Her two thousand strong goat herd and the work they do to successfully control noxious weeds is part of a system known as Alternative Weed Strategies. This non-toxic land care approach sent me on a search to learn more about these magical creatures and how to integrate their services in a closed loop regenerative system.

My friend, Kevin Johnson of Narrasys, introduced me to Biochar, a multi-layered regenerative technique, also known as *terra petra* in the Amazon. It instigated a search which led me to Wikipedia and the contribution of several researchers on this topic. The information I share in *Terra Bella* is the distillation of these researchers' work in this area as well as information gleaned from Permaculture News: Terra Petra in the Amazon, Tobias Roberts, 2017.

The information on seed procurement and dispersal, Andean rituals and cultural practices as they relate to planting and harvesting was also sourced from Wikipedia/ Andean Agriculture/ Peru Terra Petra/Yana Allpa.

I wish to express my thanks to *The Permaculture Education Center of Planet People Passion* who work in collaboration with the Peruvian-based non-profit organization *The Amazonian Institute for the Preservation of the Rainforest and Indigenous Cultures* who have established a multi-layered agro-forestry program who also aim to preserve the ancestral shamanic traditions of the Amazon, its medicinal plants and the techniques of *terra petra*.

My characters' discussion of *quipus* was based on my research on this ancient and fascinating Andean form of record keeping and the collection of data is attributed to Frank L. Salomon, author of *The Cord Keepers*. Duke University Press, Durham, NC. 2004.

Many thanks to the makers of the documentary *Love Thy Nature;* to Josh Tikell for his book, *Kiss the Ground* and the subsequent documentary. These films and others reach many people across the globe; I wish to extend many thanks to UPLIFT, an Australia-based organization, focused on positive news and events around the world and yes, whose aim is to uplift us all.

• ACKNOWLEDGEMENTS •

The artwork that Julia finds displayed in a gallery window on the streets of Istanbul is the work of Rahileh Roksari, a Persian artist whose work I encountered at *The Longworth Gallery* in Santa Fe, New Mexico

The *Icaros* referred to in my story are from *Woven Songs of the Amazon: Healing Icaros of the Shipibo Shamans,* a Fast Horse recording produced by Barrett Martin and Luis Guerra. May 2004.

I wish to thank my dearest friend, Lorene Stutzman, who has been along for the entire journey as *Terra Bella* came to life. She provided encouragement and support all along the way. Lastly, I wish to thank Dr. Joe Dispenza. Without his contagious passion and influence, this book would not have been written.

Monique Theoret
Santa Fe, 2020

Endnotes

Berry, Wendell. *The Unsettling of America.* San Francisco: Sierra Club Books, 1977.

Coleman, Eliot. *The New Organic Grower.* Vermont: Chelsea Green Publishing, 2018.

Dillard, Annie. *Pilgrim at Tinker Creek.* New York: Harper's Magazine Press, 1974.

Fukuoka, Masanobu. *The One Straw Revolution:An Introduction to Natural Farming.* Pennsylvania: Rodale Press, 1978.

Mollison, Bill. *Permaculture: A Designer's Manual.* Tasmania: Tagari Publications, 1988.

Steiner, Rudolf and Hugh Courtney. *What is Biodynamics?: A Way to Heal and Revitalize the Earth.* Massachusetts: Steiner Books, 2005.

Glossary

Biochar: charcoal produced from plant matter. When stored in the soil is a means of removing carbon dioxide from the atmosphere.

Biomimicry: the design and production of materials, structures and systems that are modeled on biological entities and processes.

Biotecture: any of several types of architecture that uses forms influenced by biological structures

Cottagecore: a term coined that indicates a return to increased self-sufficiency and the work and live balance. *Cottagecore* emphasizes simplicity and the peacefulness of pastoral life.

Earthship Biotecture: designed to produce water, electricity and food for its own use. Earthships are defined by six basic principles, all of which take advantage of the existing natural phenomena of the earth:

- Building with natural and repurposed materials
- Using thermal and solar heating and cooling
- Solar and wind-generated electricity
- Water harvesting
- Contained sewage treatment
- Self-sustained food production

Friluftsliv: a Norwegian lifestyle approach. The expression literally translates as: *open-air living*, celebrating time spent outside regardless of season or weather conditions.

Gramdan: a village gift movement originating in India inspired by Gandhi. Its foundation rests on autonomous, self-reliant villages.

Griot: a member of a class of traveling poets, musicians and storytellers who maintain a tradition of oral history in parts of West Africa.

Ikaros/Icaros: a South American indigenous colloquialism for magic song or medicine song. Today it is commonly used to describe traditional artisanal patterns of the Shipibo tribe.

madre Tierra: meaning Mother Earth in Spanish.

Mapacho: a sacred tobacco that is traditionally used in ceremonies often to clear the energetic air prior to setting intentions. A very potent variety of tobacco that has both a grounding and stimulating effect.

Meraki: a Greek word meaning doing something with soul, creativity and love.

Moshav: a unique type of cooperative farmers' village invented in Israel.

Pashmina: a fine wool made from the undercoat of domestic Himalayan goats also known as Cashmere goats.

Quechua: aboriginal people of South America who speak the Quechua languages that originated in Peru.

Sema: the ceremony performed by the Semazen. It represents *the human being's spiritual journey*, an ascent by means of intelligence and love to *Perfection*. The ceremony is performed as a remembrance of God.

Semazen: the name of the Whirling Dervishes in Sufi tradition.

Shamanism: the word derives from the Manchu-Tungus word *Saman*, to know. A shaman therefore is *one who knows*. Shamanism itself is not tied to any single culture, but experts say the shaman originated from the Tungus tribe in Siberia. The shaman interacts with a spirit world through altered states of consciousness. The goal is to direct these spiritual energies into the physical world, generally for the purpose of healing.

Tat: a comb used by Mongolian shepherds to harvest the fine wool undercoat of the Cashmere goat.

Terra Petra: meaning *Black Earth* in Portuguese, is a soil building technique developed by ancient Amazonian civilizations at least 7000 years ago to permanently solve the problems of poor tropical soil fertility. *Terra Petra* is the origin of what is presently known as *Biochar*.

Vaastu: a Sanskrit term that translates to *the science of architecture*. It is also known as *the yoga of design*. Literally, *Vaastu*, means a place where you live or dwell. Buildings using these principles are said to provide a healthier living space and a better energy balance.